Freshwater
Algae
in Australia

A Guide to Conspicuous Genera

**Timothy J. Entwisle, Jason A. Sonneman
and Simon H. Lewis**

Freehand drawings by Enid Mayfield

Royal Botanic
Gardens
Melbourne

ROYAL
BOTANIC
GARDENS
MELBOURNE

CRC for Freshwater
Ecology
Monash University

RESEARCH
COOPERATIVE CENTRE FOR
■ FRESHWATER ECOLOGY ■

Supported by The R.E. Ross Trust

Watts River, Victoria

Published by: Sainty and Associates Pty Ltd
PO Box 1219, Potts Point,
NSW 2011, Australia
Phone: (02) 9332 2661   Fax: (02) 9331 5372

ISBN 0 646 31408 4

Freshwater Algae in Australia

Entwisle, Timothy J.

Sonneman, Jason A.

Lewis, Simon H.

Design and Production: Leslie McCullough, Kathryn Duchatel.

Edited by: Jenny Haskins.

Printed by: South China Printing Co (1988) Ltd. 1997.

> *Front Cover:* Coxs River, NSW, 1996 (G.R. Sainty).
>
> *Back Cover:* Jugiong River, NSW. **Authors:** Jason Sonneman (top left), Simon Lewis (top right), Tim Entwisle.

Contents

Acknowledgements

This guide is heavily indebted to *Aquatic Cryptogams of Australia* (Entwisle 1994), a publication only made possible by the support of the Australian Society for Limnology. The R.E. Ross Trust kindly provided financial support for this and other freshwater algal projects at the Royal Botanic Gardens Melbourne, in particular providing a salary for the third author. The Royal Botanic Gardens Melbourne and the Co-operative Research Centre for Freshwater Ecology supported the first two authors respectively.

Thanks also to the many others who have assisted by providing material for illustration and/or providing logistics support: Christopher Bolch (University of Tasmania); Peter Breen (Melbourne Water/CRC Freshwater Ecology); David Cartwright, Russell Dunne, Frank Lawless, Colin Woodbridge (Melbourne Water); Kumar Eliza (Water Ecoscience); Andrea Keleher; Joan Powling; Jim Ross, Neville Walsh (Royal Botanic Gardens, Melbourne); John West (University of Melbourne).

Thanks to Dan McInnes and Ray Power for discovering and collecting algae as well as providing valuable feedback, and to Surrey Jacobs (National Herbarium of NSW) and Mark Edlund (University of Michigan) for their critical comments on the text. It has been a pleasure to work with our publisher, Sainty and Associates. Geoff Sainty, Leslie McCullough and Kathryn Duchatel have been enthusiastic and supportive throughout. It was Geoff's suggestion and insistence that we write this book, and we thank him for his concept and conviction.

Enid Mayfield executed all black and white free-hand illustrations. Simon Lewis produced all computer-generated diagrams. Photographs were provided by Peter Tyler (*Chrysonephele*); Elsa Kusel-Fetzmann (*Botrydium, Hildenbrandia*); Geoff Sainty (*Tabellaria, Spirogyra, Cladophora, Enteromorpha, Batrachospermum, Microcystis, Rivularia*); Rod Brayne (*Hydrodictyon*); Wendy Van Dok (*Nodularia* bloom); David Hill (*Cryptomonas*); Tim Spurck (*Micrasterias*); Neville Walsh (pink-coloured snow) and the remainder by Jason Sonneman and Tim Entwisle. Medical Illustrations, Monash University, provided assistance with some photographs.

Introduction

Freshwater algae undoubtedly have an image problem. We tend to think of reservoirs poisoned by toxic blue-green algal blooms, a neighbour's pool turning pea-green, or of slippery stepping stones in a river crossing. But these three plights account for only a dozen or so species of freshwater algae. Most of the over 3000 species reported from Australia are either too small to see without a hand lens or microscope, or else they inconspicuously occupy habitats ranging from waterfalls to wetlands.

We do not know how many species of freshwater algae grow in Australia. The total of 3000 plus comes from the recently published *Bibliographic Checklist of Non-marine Algae in Australia* (Day *et al.* 1995). All entries in this checklist are from literature records, many of which are unverifiable. Also many habitats remain unsampled or only partly so, and presumably many species therefore undiscovered.

This guide builds upon the chapter on macroalgae in *Aquatic Cryptogams of Australia* (Entwisle 1994), extending the coverage to include major genera of microalgae and extending its utility by incorporating colour pictures and a schematic key, and customising the text. Of the 400 or so genera reported from Australia, 96 are covered in detail by this guide. Included are all so-called macroalgae (those algae visible to the naked eye) and the most commonly reported microalgae.

The identification keys and photographs provided here use the most readily observable characters available, but as you drop in taxonomic level (towards the species) the characteristic features, by necessity, become microscopic. Algae can seldom be identified without a hand lens, and in most cases, a microscope of some sort. This should be seen as a challenge rather than an impediment, with the prize a diverse and wonderful world hidden from most people.

Algae are a vital part of the aquatic ecosystem, providing food and shelter for other organisms. They play a crucial role in the ability of an aquatic system to absorb nutrients and heavy metals, even if in some cases they cause a deterioration in water quality themselves. As a major part of the world's biodiversity, algae contain a vast array of different biochemistries, morphologies and life cycles. What is more, they are often spectacularly beautiful under the microscope.

How to use this book

To identify an unknown alga, use either the schematic key on pages 20–29 used, the description and illustrations provided should be checked carefully before confirming an identification. Note that not all genera reported from Australia are included in this guide. We have concentrated on the commonly encountered or most visible inhabitants of non-marine waters. A few 'fringe-dwellers' (e.g. those algae growing on occasionally submerged mud) also get a mention.

Schematic key

This pictorial key is designed to group together genera sharing key diagnostic features. These groupings do not reflect evolutionary or taxonomic relationships. The diagnostic features of the major groups are visible with a 10X hand lens or dissecting microscope, but within-group characters mostly require a compound microscope (with magnifications of 40X–1000X). The groups are colour-coded, corresponding to the coloured box on the margin of the photograph pages.

Page layout

Each opening contains information about one genus or, less commonly, a small group of related genera. The colour photographs of one or more species are representative of the genus but do not depict the full range of diversity. If no material was available for photographing, a drawing is provided.

Habitat: Freshwater habitats are often ephemeral or seasonally variable (e.g. a stream may become a series of pools or swamps) so an alga may be found occasionally in what appears to be an atypical habitat.

Colour: The common appellation of colour given to algae (e.g. 'red algae') can be misleading since it refers to a taxonomic category (in this case the Rhodophyta) rather than to any universal characteristic of the group. Colour can be extremely variable in some algae, often depending on features of the habitat (e.g. light irradiance) and the age of the individual. However, colour can be a useful diagnostic feature.

Habit: The alga is described in general terms, with particular emphasis on any macroscopic features such as the shape and size of the colony or tuft.

Microscopic features: A compound microscope (providing magnifications of 40X–1000X) will be essential for examining most of these features. A few, e.g. some chloroplasts, may be visible with a good quality dissecting microscope (providing magnifications of 10X–40X. Only features useful in generic identification are included (e.g. reproductive structures are not described if they are rarely encountered or do not assist in determining the correct genus).

Cell of *Chlamydomonas* (top) and *Spirogyra* (middle), and filament of *Anabaena* (bottom).

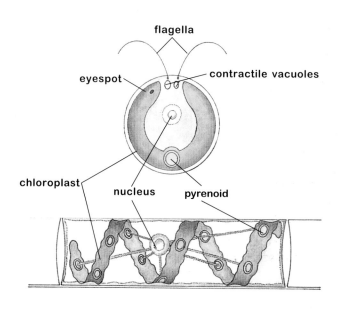

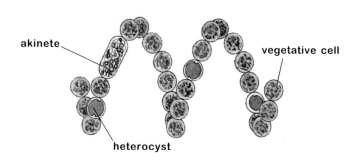

Classification: The classification of algae at higher levels (e.g. kingdom) is currently in flux, but the division and family remain useful taxonomic categories.

Species & distribution: The number of species recognized in a genus is often nebulous and the estimates given here come from major text-books and monographs, with additions from other scientific literature where appropriate. The world distribution is based on similar sources.

Only two or three of the most commonly reported species are listed by name. The distribution data are always fragmentary and the States listed here will usually represent a conservative estimate of the real extent of the species. References cited in the chapter 'Further Information' (p. 226) should be consulted to confirm any species level identification.

Notes: Information is provided on the environmental impact, rareness or any other feature of the genus not covered by the above categories. General comments about abundance and distribution are based on published data supplemented where possible by personal observations.

Compare with: Algae listed here are likely to be confused with the genus under consideration. Some will be only superficially similar while others will be close evolutionary relatives.

Captions: No species names are included. It would be misguided and misleading to do so without documenting the diagnostic features for all species in Australia. Due to a general lack of taxonomic revisions, such information is currently unavailable. In any case, it is well beyond the scope of this guide. Sometimes similar genera that are not treated separately in this guide are illustrated.

Icons: The icons along the right-hand edge of the photograph page are taken from the schematic key to groups. The first three icons along the bottom edge indicate whether you need only the naked eye, a hand lens or a microscope to identify the genus. The other two icons indicate whether the alga is microscopic (i.e. it cannot be seen in the field) or macroscopic (i.e. it can be picked up out of the water or from a rock). More than one of the latter five categories may be applicable.

What are Algae?

The term 'alga' is one of convenience and it includes simple photosynthetic organisms not included among the mosses, liverworts (and other bryophytes) or the vascular plants. Strictly, the algae are either unicellular organisms or, if multicellular, with one-celled sporangia (they never produce multicellular embryos inside the female reproductive organ).

In recent years, the simple division of the living world into 'plants' and 'animals' has been replaced by a more accurate and ultimately useful suite of kingdoms. The eukaryotic algae (those with compartmentalized cells) are part of a diverse group of organisms called protists. The kingdom Protista (once included partly in the animal kingdom and partly in the plant kingdom) is now divided into a number of as yet not adequately circumscribed kingdoms. The prokaryotic algae (the cyanobacteria) are included with bacteria in the kingdom Monera.

Following the system adopted by Day *et al.* (1995), there are 13 divisions of algae represented in Australian inland waters (a freshwater Phaeophyta has been discovered since publication of that checklist). Each division includes a wide range of vegetative and reproductive diversity, and in some cases almost identical taxa may reside in two different divisions: similar environmental pressures may have led to the evolution of similar traits in organisms with a fundamentally different origin. Not all divisions are represented in this book.

BACILLARIOPHYTA (DIATOMS)

The single cells, colonies or filaments are yellow to light brown. The cell wall always consists of two overlapping silica shells (like a petri-dish).

Acanthoceras	*Aulacoseira*	*Cyclotella*
Fragilaria	*Gomphonema*	*Tabellaria*
Urosolenia		

CHLOROPHYTA (GREEN ALGAE, INCLUDING DESMIDS)

The single cells, colonies, filaments or more complexly structured algae are usually grass-green. Motile cells have usually two or four anterior flagella of equal length. This division includes many distinct evolutionary lineages.

Ankistrodesmus	*Botryococcus*	*Bulbochaete*
Chaetophora	*Chara*	*Chlamydomonas*

Cladophora	Closterium	Coleochaete
Cosmarium	Cylindrocapsa	Dichotomosiphon
Dictyosphaerium	Draparnaldia	Elakatothrix
Enteromorpha	Gonium	Hyalotheca
Hydrodictyon	Klebsormidium	Micractinium
Micrasterias	Microspora	Monostroma
Mougeotia	Nitella	Oedogonium
Oocystis	Palmellopsis	Palmodictyon
Parallela	Pediastrum	Pithophora
Pseudosphaerocystis	Radiofilum	Rhizoclonium
Scenedesmus	Schizochlamys	Schizomeris
Sphaeroplea	Spirogyra	Staurastrum
Stichococcus	Stigeoclonium	Tetraspora
Tetrasporidium	Ulothrix	Volvox
Zygnema		

CHRYSOPHYTA (GOLDEN-BROWN ALGAE)

The single cells, colonies or filaments are yellow, golden-brown or rarely green. Motile cells usually have two anterior flagella of unequal length.

Chrysonephele	Dinobryon	Mallomonas
Synura	Tetrasporopsis	

CRYPTOPHYTA (CRYPTOMONADS)

The single cells are red, blue-green or olive-brown. All cells are motile, usually with two slightly unequal flagella.

Cryptomonas

CYANOBACTERIA (BLUE-GREEN ALGAE)

The single cells, colonies and more complexly structured algae are blue-green, brownish, olive-green or rarely bright green. The cells are without compartments (no membrane-bound organelles): in particular there is no nuclear region defined by a membrane and photosynthetic pigments are distributed throughout the cells (not in chloroplasts). Sexual reproduction and motile cells are absent.

Anabaena	Coleodesmium	Loefgrenia
Lyngbya	Microcoleus	Microcystis
Nodularia	Nostoc	Oscillatoria
Phormidium	Pseudanabaena	Rivularia
Schizothrix	Scytonema	Spirulina
Stigonema	Tolypothrix	

DINOPHYTA (DINOFLAGELLATES)

The single cells are brown or brownish green. Motile cells have a prominent transverse furrow in which two flagella are inserted (one encircling the cell transversely, the other extending from the cell).

Peridinium

EUGLENOPHYTA (EUGLENOIDS)

The single cells are green (sometimes colourless) with a red 'eyespot'. The motile cells usually have two flagella inserted in a 'gullet' at the anterior end of the cell, one shorter flagella often non-emergent.

Euglena   *Phacus*   *Trachelomonas*

GLAUCOPHYTA

The single cells or colonies are blue-green. The pigments are held in symbiotic blue-green algal cells rather than chloroplasts (possibly representing an earlier stage in chloroplast evolution). The motile cells are bilaterally symmetrical with two lateral flagella.

None in this guide.

PHAEOPHYTA (BROWN ALGAE)

Almost entirely comprised of marine species. The filaments are brownish or yellow-brown. Motile cells usually have two unequal flagella.

Ectocarpus

PRYMNESIOPHYTA (HAPTOPHYTES)

The single cells, colonies or filaments are golden-brown. Motile cells have two more-or-less equal flagella and a thread-like organelle (the haptonema) between them.

None in this guide.

RAPHIDOPHYTA

Algae similar to Tribophytes but with a distinctive internal cell structure.

None in this guide.

RHODOPHYTA (RED ALGAE)

Predominantly (c. 95% of species) marine. The single cells, filaments or more complexly structured algae are red, brown, olive-green or more rarely grass-green. There are no motile cells in this division and sexual reproduction is often remarkably complex. Most have characteristic

Lake Pedder, Tasmania

Farmland swamp, Gippsland

Old River, Tasmania

Three different algal habitats

microscopic connections between the vegetative cells, although the blue-green alga *Stigonema* appears to have similar connections, and the red alga *Compsopogon* has connections that are too small to be seen under normal light microscopy.

Audouinella	*Batrachospermum*	*Bostrychia*
Caloglossa	*Chroodactylon*	*Compsopogon*
Hildenbrandia	*Psilosiphon*	*Ptilothamnion*

TRIBOPHYTA (YELLOW-GREEN ALGAE)

The single cells or filaments (sometimes without cross-walls, i.e. siphonous) are green or yellow-green. Motile cells have two anterior flagella of unequal length.

Botrydium	*Tribonema*	*Vaucheria*

Habitats

Algae grow in almost every habitat in every part of the world. The following are examples of non-marine (loosely termed 'freshwater' here) habitats.

Animals: Reported substrates include turtles, snails, rotifers, worms, crustacea and many other animals (e.g. alligators and three-toed sloths are hosts outside Australia). Freshwater sponges and some other animals (e.g. infusoria, rhizopods) have symbiotic relationships with algae.

Aquatic plants: Algae grow on and inside water plants (including other algae), but are generally not restricted to a single host. However, *Anabaena* is commonly found inside the aquatic fern *Azolla*.

'Artificial' substrates: Wooden posts and fences, cans and bottles etc. all provide algal habitats.

Billabongs & lagoons: These are often rich microalgal habitats, particularly for desmids. Their ecology is poorly understood and changes in flooding regime may alter the algal flora.

Bogs, marshes & swamps: These too can be rich desmid habitats (e.g. *Sphagnum* bogs).

Farm Dams: These 'artificial' water-bodies may allow taxa to extend their 'natural' range.

Hot springs: Little is known of hot springs algae in Australia, but as elsewhere the blue-green algae (Cyanobacteria) dominate except where sulfide concentrations in the water are high.

Lakes: Coloured (or humic) lakes are usually species-rich but are uncommon in most of Australia. All lakes have a floating (or swimming) microalgal flora and an 'attached' micro- and macro-algal flora.

Mud and sand: The surface of submerged soil in shallow waters supports many species.

Ponds (ephemeral), puddles, roadside ditches and rock pools: Little studied in Australia.

Reservoirs: Well-established reservoirs with protected catchments provide ideal habitat for many microalgae, particularly desmids. So-called 'protected' catchments have world-wide value given the paucity of such systems overseas.

Rivers: Very few lowland rivers are in a pristine state, and they tend to have few algal species. Upland rivers can have an algal flora similar to their tributaries.

Rock (internal): An intriguing habitat where algae grow within porous rocks (e.g. Australian Antarctic Territory).

Rock (surface): Little studied in Australia.

Saline & Hypersaline Lagoons: These mostly coastal habitats have an intriguing microalgal flora but are very sensitive to changes in the water table.

Saline Lakes & Marshes: Such habitats are species-poor, but have a distinctive algal flora (e.g. lakes in the Victorian Volcanic Plains).

Salt marshes and salt lakes: Again not a strictly 'fresh' water habitat, but a distinctive non-marine one. On mud around and in salt lakes and saline channels, *Vaucheria* is usually common, at least in the wetter months. *Enteromorpha, Cladophora* and *Rhizoclonium* also grow in brackish to saline waters.

Snow: 'Red or pink snow' is usually coloured by *Chlamydomonas*, but other algae can grow in this habitat.

Soil: The algal species composition of cryptogam mats (e.g. in dry country and grassland) is largely unknown, but such mats are of great environmental importance. *Anabaena* grows in nodules formed on the surface roots of cycads.

Streams: Acidic streams support a diverse macroalgal flora and are highly susceptible to impaction, eutrophication and river engineering. Alkaline streams are not common naturally in Australia. They seem to be species-poor, but due to restricted occurrence they may support rare taxa. Eutrophic streams are species-poor, but sometimes native taxa remain and, due to a lack of oligotrophic streams in some areas, they may represent the last fragments of a previously wide distribution.

Terrestrial plants: *Trentepohlia* and related species have a very similar habit to lichens growing on tree trunks and branches. *Apatococcus* (previously included in the more broadly circumscribed *Protococcus*) is universally common as a green powdery covering on the shady side of trees. Algae also live on the surface of, or penetrate into, leaves; it is possible that such species are extremely diverse in rainforests. Closer to the ground, the blue-green alga *Nostoc* grows inside the thallus of some hornworts (moss-like plants). Lichens, a symbiosis between algae and fungi, usually contain green algae (particularly *Trebouxia* and less commonly *Trentepohlia*) or sometimes blue-green algae (e.g. *Nostoc, Scytonema, Stigonema*). Other plant habitats, not studied in Australia, include tree hollows and pitcher plants. Terrestrial algae are not considered further in this volume.

A saline lake near Yorketown SA, turned pink by a bloom of *Dunaliella*.

Collecting algae

Collection methods

Macroalgae and the attached microalgae can be collected by hand or with a knife, including part or all of the substrate (rock, plant, wood etc.) if possible. Search all habitats in the waterbody including the edge of stones in fast-flowing water, aquatic plants, dam walls, and any floating debris. In running or slightly turbid waters, a simple viewing box made from transparent perspex enables attached algae to be more easily observed. A hand lens is often useful to determine if material is reproductive (essential for species determination in some genera and helpful for generic placement).

Microscopic floating algae (the phytoplankton) can be collected with a mesh net (e.g. with 25–30 μm pores) or, if in sufficient quantity (i.e. colouring the water), by simply scooping a jar through the water. Water samples can be left overnight allowing the algae to settle and concentrate on the bottom of the container. Squeezing *Sphagnum* and other mosses, or some aquatic flowering plants such as *Utricularia*, is a good way to collect a large number of species.

Microscope slides suspended in a waterbody for c. 2–4 weeks will reveal many species. The slides should be kept submerged until ready to examine under the microscope. One side can be wiped clean and a coverslip placed over the other.

Algae growing on soil are difficult to collect and study, many requiring culturing before sufficient and suitable material is available for identification.

Storage and preservation

Algae can be stored initially in a bucket, jar, bottle or plastic bag, with some water from the collecting site. The container should be left open or only half-filled with liquid, and wide shallow containers are better than narrow deep jars. Note that glass is reportedly not satisfactory for some Chrysophyta and other algae of acidic waters due to its inherent alkalinity damaging cells. However, glass phials are commonly used to collect algae. If refrigerated or kept on ice soon after collecting most algae can be kept alive for short periods (a day or two). If relatively sparse in the sample, some algae can continue to grow in an open dish stored in a cool place with reduced light (traditionally a south-facing window in the Southern Hemisphere). For long-term storage, specimens can be preserved in liquid (see below), dried, or made into a permanent microscope mount (preferably all three). Even with ideal preservation, examination of fresh material is sometimes essential for an accurate determination. Motile algae particularly must be examined while flagella and other delicate structures remain intact.

Liquid preservation

Commercial formalin (which is a solution of 40% formaldehyde), diluted between 1/10 and 1/20 with the collecting solution, is the most commonly used fixative. Note that formaldehyde is thought to be carcinogenic and all contact with skin, eyes and air passages should be avoided. FAA (by volume, 40% formaldehyde *1*: glacial acetic acid *1*: 95% alcohol *8*: water *10*) or ' 6-3-1' (by volume, water *6*: 90% alcohol *3*: 40% formaldehyde *1*) solutions give better preservation results for some of the more fragile algae, whereas the standard alcohol and water mix (e.g. 70% ethyl alcohol or industrial methylated spirit) will ruin all but the larger algae.

Algae can be kept in diluted formalin for a number of years, but the solution is usually replaced by 70% ethyl alcohol with 5% glycerin (the latter to prevent accidental drying out).

Lugol's solution is commonly used for short-term (e.g. a few months, but possibly a year or more) storage of microalgae. Dissolve one gram of iodine crystals and two grams of potassium iodide in 300 ml of water. Use three drops of this solution in a 100 ml sample (it should look like very weak tea).

Dried herbarium specimens

Dried herbarium specimens can be prepared by 'floating out' similar to aquatic flowering plants. Ideally, fresh specimens should be fixed prior to drying. Most algae will adhere to absorbent herbarium paper. Smaller, more fragile specimens or tangled, mat-forming algae may be dried onto mica or cellophane. After 'floating out', most freshwater algae should not be pressed but simply left to air dry in a warm dry room. If pressed, they should be covered with a piece of waxed paper, plastic or muslin cloth so that the specimen does not stick to the drying paper in the press.

To examine a dried herbarium specimen add a few drops of water to the specimen. After a minute or so the specimen will swell and lift slightly from the paper. Carefully remove a small portion of the specimen with forceps or a razor-blade.

Collection information

Record collector's name and collection number, and as many of the following features as possible: whether the water is saline, brackish or fresh; whether the collection site is terrestrial, or a river, stream or lake; whether the alga is submerged during water level fluctuations or floods; whether the water is muddy or polluted; whether the alga is free-floating or attached, and if the latter, the type of substrate to which it is attached; and the colour, texture and size of the alga.

Microscopy and microscopes

Examining fresh material

Observations (preferably including drawings or photographs) based on living material are essential for the identification of some genera and a valuable adjunct to more leisurely observations on preserved material for others. The simplest method is to place of drop of the water including the alga onto a microscope slide and carefully lower a coverslip onto it. It is always tempting to put a large amount of the alga onto the slide but smaller fragments are much easier to view under a microscope. Start by observing the alga at lower magnification (40X or 100X) and move sequentially up if necessary. Microalgae may be better observed using the 'hanging drop method': place a few drops of the sample liquid on a coverslip and turn it over onto a ring of paraffin wax, liquid paraffin or a 'slide ring'.

Permanent slides

A permanent slide is a valuable addition to wet and dry herbarium specimens. Analine blue (1% aqueous solution with 4% molar HCl), Toluidine blue O (0.05% aqueous solution) and Potassium permangenate (2% aqueous $KMnO_4$) are useful stains for macroalgae (different stains suit different species), and Indian Ink is a good stain for highlighting mucilage and some flagella-like structures.

After staining for 30 seconds to five minutes (depending on the material), rinse in water, then add a drop or two of 10% corn syrup solution (Karo™ corn syrup with the addition of 2% phenol) to a small piece of the alga placed on a microscope slide, then carefully lower the coverslip. (A corn syrup solution of 5% or less may be required for the more fragile species.) Add drops of 40% corn syrup solution at the side of the coverslip as the liquid underneath the coverslip evaporates. Once 'set' (i.e. solid but often still sticky), the sides of the coverslip can be readily sealed with nail polish.

Glycerine solution (75% glycerine, 25% water) is another useful mounting agent and should be introduced in a similar manner to the corn syrup, i.e. starting with a very dilute solution and building up to 100% glycerine. Sealing with nail polish is essential.

These two mountants are unsuitable for most unicellular algae which should be examined fresh or in temporary mounts of liquid-preserved material.

Microscopes

Magnifications of between 40 and 1000 times are required for the identification of all but a few algal genera. A compound microscope is therefore an essential piece of equipment for anyone wishing to discover the full extent of algal diversity. Student microscopes with 10X eyepiece and 4X–10X–40X objectives are available for about $500 and such a microscope would be suitable for identifying all algae in this guide. An oil immersion 100X objective, available for about $90, would be a useful addition, particularly when identifying to species level. A camera lucida attachment is helpful for producing accurate drawings, while an eyepiece micrometer is important for any species-level identifications. Phase-contrast or interference (e.g. Nomarski) microscopy can improve the image for bleached or small specimens, but these are available only on more expensive microscope systems.

A dissecting microscope providing magnifications up to 40 or 50 times is a useful aid but is secondary to a compound microscope. High quality dissecting microscopes cost between $1500 (without light source) to fully integrated systems with a built-in light source at about $3500. Dissecting microscopes costing less than $1500, either of lower quality or with a reduced range of magnifications, may be suitable for some purposes. An adequate 20X or 40X system can be bought for $300.

Scanning and transmission electron microscopes are beyond the reach of all but specialist institutions but are an essential tool for identifying some of the very small algae. None of the algae illustrated here require electron microscopy for identification to genus.

Freshwater algal management

Blooms

When microscopic algae flourish to such an extent that they colour the water, which eventually becomes soup-like, they are said to be blooming. Some of the genera known to form toxic blooms in Australia are *Anabaena*, *Cylindrospermopsis*, *Microcystis*, *Nodularia* and occasionally *Oscillatoria* (or *Planktothrix*).

While many factors are known to influence the growth and survival of algae (e.g. light, temperature, turbidity, nutrients, salinity, pH, grazing), the exact factors or combination of factors that trigger algal blooms in Australia are yet little understood. Blooms of blue-green algae generally grow in nutrient-rich, calm, warm water. The ability of many blue-green species to regulate their position in the water column, and to fix atmospheric nitrogen confers to them a competitive advantage over other algae in phosphate replete, but nitrogen deplete conditions that often characterize Australian waters. It has been argued (Jones 1994) that lack of mixing (stratification) of a water body rather than excessive nutrient pollution is the key trigger for algal blooms. Temperature stratification is a common phenomenon in Australia during hot summer months. It is conceivable that the building of reservoirs and weirs is of as much, if not of more, importance than nutrient pollution in the prevalence of blue-green algal blooms in Australia. However, nutrient pollution and possible lack of diverse aquatic biota will exacerbate the problem.

General guidelines for the prevention and management of algal blooms can be found in Jones (1994), some of which are summarized below. Prevention of blue-green algal blooms in many cases may be directly related to the causal factors. Stratification in lakes and reservoirs can be prevented by producing turbulence with aerators or mechanical mixers. Well mixed waters minimise the release of nutrients from the sediment, disperse blue-green algal blooms and encourage the growth of other algae such as diatoms and green algae. Many river systems also stratify during low flows, and require minimum environmental releases of water for containment of algal blooms. Management of nutrient sources such as treatment of effluent from sewage treatment plants and rural industries, refinement of land management practices, and improved urban stormwater management will all help to reduce the severity of algal blooms.

Copper-based algicides (at doses of up to one mg copper per litre) offer a short-term solution, but copper is a persistent environmental pollutant. In addition, there is usually a massive release of toxins into the water following the use of this poison, as well as high oxygen demands as the algal biomass decomposes. Algicides should be used (under strict guidance) only when the waterbody is essential for the provision of drinking water for humans or stock.

Alternative chemicals, whether 'artificial' or 'natural' (e.g. from barley straw), and biomanipulation methods require further testing. In general it is advisable to allow a big algal bloom to run its natural course. All contact with the water should be avoided and the area clearly signed. The bloom will eventually disperse and native aquatic ecosystems will remain in better shape than if the bulldozer approach of algicides were used. All blue-green blooms should be reported to your State water authority.

Weeds

Macroalgae can choke rivers, channels and lakes, resulting in aesthetic or economic damage. In urban creeks, the filamentous green algae *Cladophora* and *Stigeoclonium* (Entwisle 1989c), and the diatom *Melosira* cause most problems. *Hydrodictyon*, and sometimes *Cladophora*, can grow in large masses in still or nearly still water, such as in irrigation and drainage channels (May 1982). *Spirogyra* and other genera in the Zygnemataceae can form floating or loosely attached masses in streams and dams. *Pithophora* and *Compsopogon* may also cause weed problems (Entwisle & Price 1992). As with blooms, eutrophication, high temperatures and slow-flowing water are conducive to problem macroalgal weed growths. Control is by physical removal of the algal mats, poisoning (as for blooms) or by long-term management strategies.

It is sometimes difficult to determine whether species are native to Australia or, if they are, whether their distribution has extended substantially due to alteration of the environment by humans (see Entwisle & Price 1992 for comments on the distribution of *Compsopogon* and *Pithophora*). Some species are almost certainly native due to their presence in pristine or near-pristine catchments: e.g. species of *Batrachospermum*, *Draparnaldia* and *Psilosiphon*. Algae tolerant of hard (calcium and magnesium rich) waters are probably now more widespread through eutrophic waters, e.g. *Cladophora* and *Stigeoclonium*, if indeed they are native to Australia.

Rare and threatened freshwater algae

Algae are important economically as a source of products such as carotene, glycerol, alginates, and as a food source for wild and cultivated fish and crustaceans. They have critical significance as carbon-fixing and oxygenating organisms. Over and perhaps above this, the freshwater algal flora of Australia has a unique character, including as it does many endemic and distinctive taxa. Each new habitat or regional sample reveals more surprises for Australian phycologists (algal specialists). Unfortunately, algal habitat is being destroyed or altered at a far greater rate than species are discovered, and the so-called 'threatening processes' are too numerous to list here. Australia's lakes, rivers, swamps and ponds are seldom safe havens for algae.

There are good distributional data for very few species in Australia, but we do know from widespread sampling for, and/or the distinctiveness of, some taxa that they are definitely uncommon. However, it is difficult to assess the abundance of most species. As an example, in 1993, of the 364 taxa of *macroalgae* reported from inland waters in Australia, 70% were known from a single locality (and collected only once), 13% from two localities and only 17% from more than two localities.

To interpret such figures, the following qualifications need to be borne in mind: when any groups of macroalgae have been comprehensively revised (only two genera to date), most early records are found to be misidentifications or a result of too narrow a species concept (most names now being considered to be synonyms of more widely distributed taxa). On the other hand, recent taxonomic work on the freshwater red algae (including examination of European type material), indicates that many more taxa are endemic than previously thought. In addition, although some Australian taxa may appear morphologically very similar to European taxa, it is possible that 'comparative iconography' (*sensu* Peter Tyler, numerous publications), is too coarse a technique to unravel the relationships between antipodean and European algae.

The status of names reported from a single locality cannot be assessed until 1) more collecting has been done (to get good distributional data) and 2) extensive taxonomic research validates the various records (where possible). It would seem, from a scientific point of view, advisable to treat all records on face-value until proven otherwise.

For practical reasons, the year 1950 was chosen as the starting date for a listing of over 200 rare, threatened or endangered taxa in the *Overview of the Conservation of Non-marine Non-vascular Plants in Australia* (1995; unpublished report to Environment Australia, Canberra). This eliminated many of the unvouchered and poorly described taxa of early this century. Undoubtedly some of these warrant protection (some earlier workers were very astute observers), but to list them all would make the list even more unworkable. As it is, most of the 200 or so species and variants of algae listed in the *Overview* as possibly rare or threatened in Australia were described from single collections as part of limited sampling of isolated areas: only seven taxa could be confidently coded as vulnerable or potentially vulnerable under the Australian and New Zealand Environment and Conservation Council (ANZECC) criteria. In few studies have phycologists attempted to collect widely and survey the range of particular species.

Pink snow on the victorian Alps caused by a bloom of *Chlamydomonas*.

Schematic Key

Group 1
(p. 30–57)
Single cells (or compact group of 1–4 cells)

Group 2
(p. 58–71)
Motile single cells

Group 3
(p. 72–99)
Unbranched filaments

Group 4
(p. 100–117)
Branched filaments

Group 5
(p. 118–123)
Siphons (no crosswalls)

Group 6
(p. 124–133)
Some filaments more than one cell thick, or tightly packed cells in a cylinder

Group 7
(p. 134–141)
Whorls of smaller branches around an axis

Group 8
(p. 142–177)
Soft or firm colony of many cells or filaments

Group 9
(p. 178–181)
Sheet or blade of tightly packed cells

Group 10
(p. 182–215)
Cyanobacteria (cells without organelles)

Ptilothamnion
(p. 216–217)
Zigzag axis

Hydrodictyon
(p. 218–219)
Netted

Hildenbrandia
(p. 220–221)
Crust-like

Group 1
(single cells)

cell shape

Cosmarium

Closterium

Micrasterias

Staurastrum (2 perspectives)

Ankistrodesmus

Tabellaria

Oocystis

Scenedesmus

Stichococcus

Cyclotella

Fragilaria

Gomphonema

Urosolenia

Acanthoceras

cell contents

Cyanobacteria
(see Group 10)

21

Group 2
(motile single cells)

cell shape

Euglena

Cryptomonas

Chlamydomonas

Phacus

Trachelomonas

Mallomonas

Peridinium

Group 3
(unbranched filaments)

chloroplasts

Ulothrix

Klebsormidium

Stichococcus
(see Group 1)

Spirogyra

cell walls

Microspora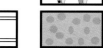

Mougeotia

cell walls

Oedogonium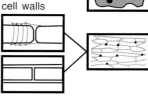

Rhizoclonium

Sphaeroplea

Zygnema,
Cylindrocapsa

Hyalotheca

Aulacoseira, Tribonema
(also see *Tabellaria* and
Fragilaria)

Radiofilum

cell contents

Cyanobacteria
(see Group 10)

23

Group 4
(branched filaments)

filament

Audouinella

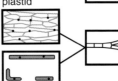

Stigeoclonium

Cladophora

plastid

Ectocarpus

Pithophora

Coleochaete

Bulbochaete

Radiofilum (see
Group 3)

plastid

Chroodactylon

Dinobryon

Cyanobacteria
(see Group 10)

cell contents

Group 5
(siphons)

siphon

Botrydium

Dichotomosiphon

Vaucheria

Group 6

(some filaments more than one cell thick, or tightly packed cells in a cylinder)

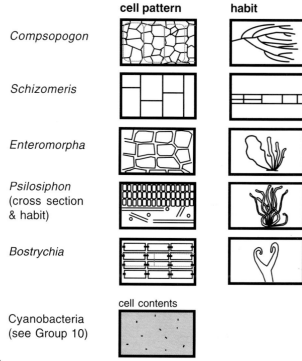

	cell pattern	habit
Compsopogon		
Schizomeris		
Enteromorpha		
Psilosiphon (cross section & habit)		
Bostrychia		

Cyanobacteria (see Group 10)

cell contents

Group 7

(whorls of smaller branches around an axis)

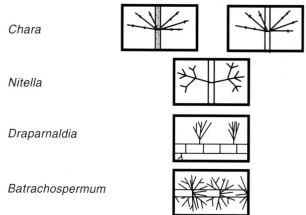

habit detail

Chara

Nitella

Draparnaldia

Batrachospermum

Group 8
(soft or firm colony of many cells or filaments)

	cell arrangement	individual cell
Tetraspora		
Palmellopsis		
Schizochlamys		
Tetrasporidium		
Parallela		
Palmodictyon		
Cosmarium (see Group 1)		
Chrysonephele		
Tetrasporopsis		
Dictyosphaerium		

Group 8
(continued)

	cell arrangement	individual cell

Elakatothrix

Oocystis
(see Group 1)

Chaetophora (see also *Coleochete*, Group 4)

Botryococcus

Pseudosphaerocystis

Micractinium

Volvox

Gonium

Synura

Pediastrum

cell contents

Cyanobacteria
(see Group 10)

Group 9
(sheet or blade of tightly packed cells)

habit

Monostroma

Caloglossa

Group 10 (Cyanobacteria)

detail

Microcystis

Stigonema

Loefgrenia

Tolypothrix

Scytonema

habit

Coleodesmium

Rivularia

Group 10
(Cyanobacteria continued)

	habit	detail
Nostoc		
Nodularia		
Anabaena		
Pseudanabaena		
Phormidium		
Oscillatoria		
Lyngbya		
Microcoleus		
Schizothrix		
Spirulina		

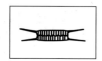

ACANTHOCERAS

Habitat: Free-floating in rivers, reservoirs and ponds.

Colour: Yellow-brownish.

Habit: This rectangular plate-like diatom, 30–80 μm long, extends into long spines at the corners.

Microscopic Features: The cell walls produce of a series of bands which interlock to form a zigzag line along the length of the cell. The chloroplasts are discoid and distributed around the middle of the cell.

Classification: Division Bacillariophyta, Family Acanthocerataceae.

Species and Distribution: One species, cosmopolitan.

Acanthoceras zachariasii: NT, NSW, Vic.

Notes: *Acanthoceras* is common in ponds and lakes but is sometimes difficult to see under bright field microscopy (if possible, use phase contrast). Previously known as *Attheya.*

Compare With: *Urosolenia.*

Caption:
Acanthoceras X 500; note that in 'side' (girdle) view, it resembles *Urosolenia.*

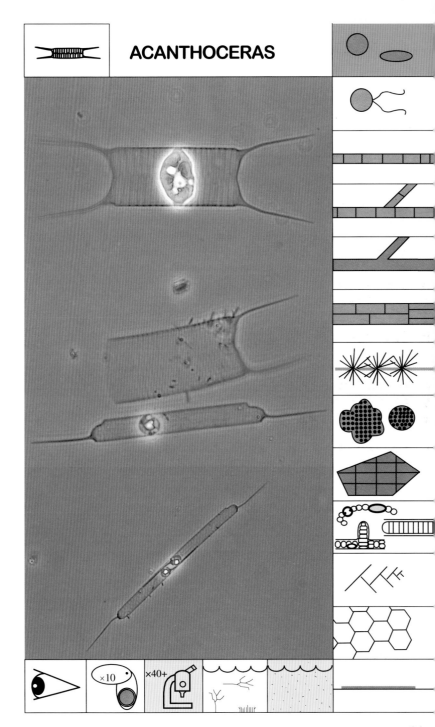

ACANTHOCERAS

 **ANKISTRODESMUS**

Habitat: Free-floating in ponds and lakes, sometimes forming blooms; also on soil.

Colour: Green.

Habit: The microscopic cells are 25–60 μm long, needle- to spindle-shaped, tapering at both ends, and may be spirally twisted.

Microscopic Features: The thin-walled cells may be solitary or aggregated in small groups and each has a plate-like chloroplastwith or without a pyrenoid.

Classification: Division Chlorophyta, Family Oocystaceae.

Species and Distribution: 20 species, cosmopolitan; nine species reported from Australia.

e.g.　*Ankistrodesmus falcatus*: cosmopolitan; WA, NT, Qld, NSW, Vic., Tas.
　　　Ankistrodesmus spiralis: cosmopolitan; NT, Qld, Tas.

Notes: *Ankistrodesmus* is widespread and common.

Compare With: None in this guide.

Caption:
Ankistrodesmus X 500 (top, centre).
Kirchneriella, a similar genus,　X 400 (bottom-left).
Actinastrum, a similar genus, X 400 (bottom-right).

ANKISTRODESMUS

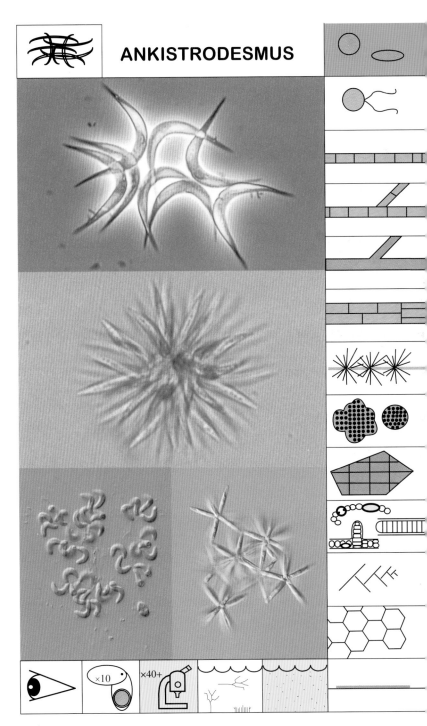

CLOSTERIUM

Habitat: Free-floating in lakes; also found among filamentous algae in streams.

Colour: Green.

Habit: This crescent-shaped desmid can be needle-like or resemble a quarter moon.

Microscopic Features: The cells are 100–1000 μm long and divided into two equal portions (semi-cells), with a single chloroplast in each; the central nucleus is prominent. The vacuoles at each pole are conspicuous.

Classification: Division Chlorophyta, Family Desmidiaceae.

Species and Distribution: c. 100 species, cosmopolitan; 68 species reported from Australia.

e.g.   *Closterium acerosum*: cosmopolitan; NT, SA, Qld, NSW, Vic., Tas.
        Closterium kuetzingii: cosmopolitan; NT, SA, Qld, NSW, Vic., Tas.
        Closterium striolatum: cosmopolitan; NT, SA, Qld, NSW, Vic., Tas.

Notes: *Closterium* is widespread and extremely diverse.

Compare With: *Ankistrodesmus.*

Caption:
Closterium X 600 (top, upper-middle, lower-middle), X 100 (bottom).

CLOSTERIUM

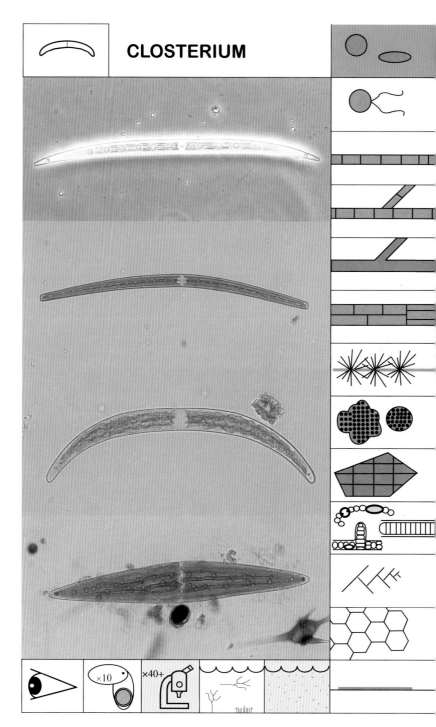

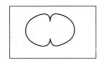

COSMARIUM

Habitat: Free-floating in lakes, reservoirs and ponds; sometimes in attached gelatinous colonies.

Colour: Green.

Habit: This free-floating or attached desmid is partly incised in the middle. It sometimes forms macroscopic gelatinous colonies.

Microscopic Features: The compressed cells, 10–160 μm long and slightly longer than broad, are divided into two equal portions (semi-cells), with a single chloroplast in each; the central nucleus is prominent. The surface of the cell walls is smooth or ornamented with granules, but without spines.

Classification: Division Chlorophyta, Family Desmidiaceae.

Species and Distribution: 1200–2000 species, cosmopolitan; c. 218 species from Australia.

e.g.   *Cosmarium askenasyi*: cosmopolitan; NT, Qld, NSW.
   Cosmarium granatum: cosmopolitan; NT, SA, Qld, NSW, Vic., Tas.
   Cosmarium punctulatum: cosmopolitan; NT, SA, Qld, NSW, Vic., Tas.

Notes: *Cosmarium* is extremely common and diverse in Australia, as it is worldwide. If there are more than two projections in each semi-cell the alga should be referred to *Staurastrum*.

Compare With: *Staurastrum*.

Caption:
Cosmarium X 400 (top-left, top-right), X 1000 (middle-left), X 400 (middle-right).
Staurodesmus, a similar desmid, X 800 (bottom-left).
Xanthidium, a similar desmid, (also cf. *Staurastrum*), X 400 (bottom-right).

COSMARIUM

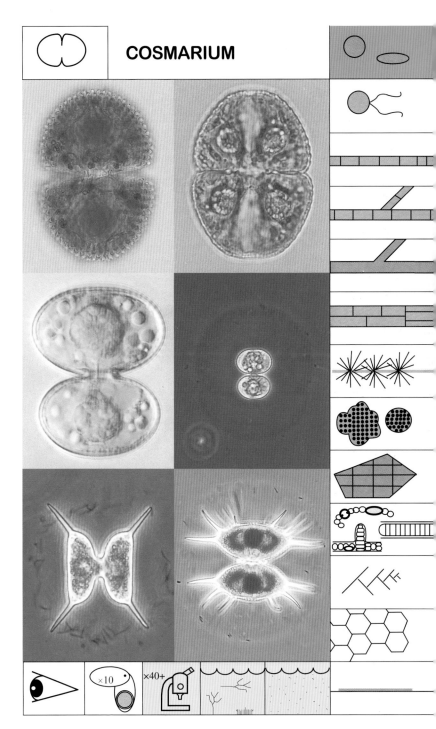

37

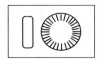

CYCLOTELLA

Habitat: Free-floating or attached to plants and rocks in fresh, brackish and salt water, in rivers and lakes.

Colour: Yellow-brown.

Habit: The diatom is discoid or drum-shaped, and 15–45 μm diameter.

Microscopic Features: The siliceous cell walls (frustules) are marked with radial lines or pits around the edge and another smooth concentric pattern inside. Each cell contains numerous discoid chloroplasts.

Classification: Division Bacillariophyta, Family Stephanodiscaceae.

Species and Distribution: 30 species, cosmopolitan;15 species reported from Australia.

e.g.   *Cyclotella stelligera*: cosmopolitan; WA, NT, Qld, NSW, Vic., Tas.

Notes: *Cyclotella* is widespread and common.

Compare With: Other 'centric' diatoms.

Caption:
Cyclotella X 1800 (top), X 2000 (middle-left), X 3500 (middle-right).
Coscinodiscus, another planktonic diatom, X 500 (bottom-left),
X 1000(bottom-right).

CYCLOTELLA

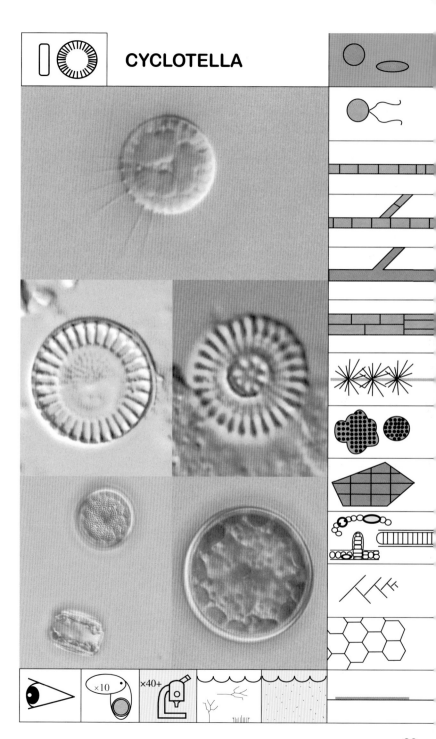

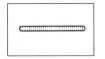

FRAGILARIA

Habitat: Free-floating or attached to stones, wood, plants or other algae; occurring in running water or ponds, lakes.

Colour: Brownish-green.

Habit: This diatom is usually straight and narrow. The cells are 25–500 μm long and may be attached side-by-side to form 'ribbon-like' chains.

Microscopic Features: A gap (pseudoraphe) is evident between the transverse markings. The cells contain two chloroplasts, often with three or more pyrenoids.

Classification: Division Bacillariophyta, Family Fragilariaceae.

Species and Distribution: c. 30 species, cosmopolitan; 32 species reported from Australia.

e.g.   *Fragilaria acus*: cosmopolitan; SA, Qld, NSW, Vic., Tas.
          Fragilaria pulchella: cosmopolitan; Qld, NSW, Vic., Tas.
          Fragilaria ulna: cosmopolitan; WA, NT, SA, Qld, NSW, Vic., Tas.

Notes: *Fragilaria* is widespread and common. Some authors divide *Fragilaria* into smaller genera and the names *Synedra ulna, S. acus* and *Ctenophora pulchella* may be used.

Compare With: *Gomphonema, Tabellaria.*

Caption:
Fragilaria X 800 (top), X 600 (upper-middle), X 800 (lower-middle), X 1000 (bottom).

FRAGILARIA

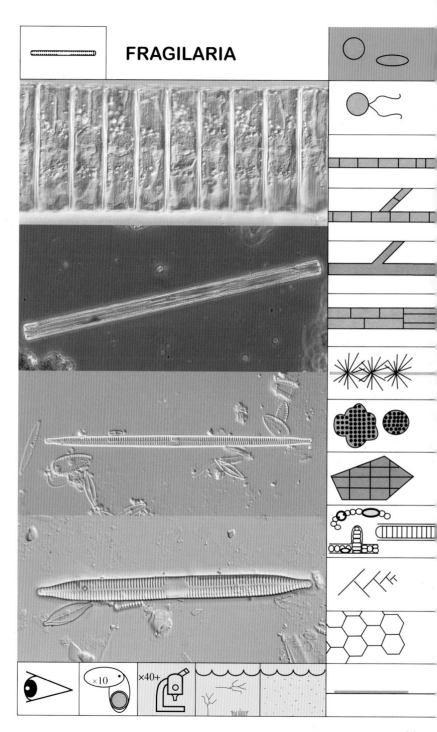

41

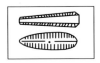

GOMPHONEMA

Habitat: Attached to rocks, plants and other algae in a diverse range of water bodies from aqueducts to rivers.

Colour: Golden-brown.

Habit: This diatom is bilaterally symmetrical, straight, and lanceolate or club-shaped. The cells sometimes terminate a branched mucilaginous stalk.

Microscopic Features: The cells are c. 20–70 μm, transversely asymmetrical in top and side view, and contain numerous discoid chloroplasts.

Classification: Division Bacillariophyta, Family Gomphonemataceae.

Species and Distribution: 50 species, cosmopolitan; 32 species reported from Australia.

e.g. *Gomphonema gracile*: cosmopolitan; WA, NT, Qld, NSW, Vic., Tas.
Gomphonema parvulum: cosmopolitan; WA, NT, SA, Qld, NSW, Vic., Tas.
Gomphonema truncatum: cosmopolitan; Qld, NSW, Vic., Tas.

Notes: *Gomphonema* is widespread and common. *Gomphonema truncatum* was previously called *G. constrictum*.

Compare With: *Tabellaria.*

Caption:
Gomphonema attached by gelatinous stalks to *Oscillatoria* (top), X 1000 (upper-middle).
Navicula, another common pennate diatom, X 1000 (lower-middle).
Cymbella, another common pennate diatom, X 1000 (bottom).

GOMPHONEMA

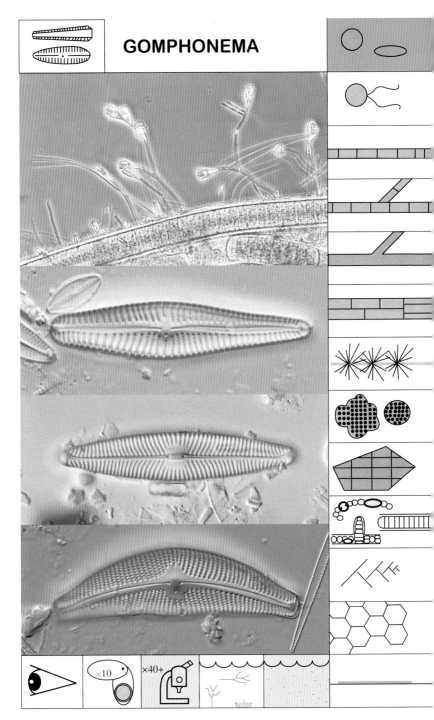

43

MICRASTERIAS

Habitat: Free-floating in lakes and reservoirs.

Colour: Green.

Habit: This desmid is variously and often spectacularly lobed.

Microscopic Features: The cells are 60–200 μm wide and divided into two equal portions (semi-cells), with a single chloroplast in each; the central nucleus is prominent.

Classification: Division Chlorophyta, Family Desmidiaceae.

Species and Distribution: 65 species, cosmopolitan; 38 species reported from Australia.

e.g.　*Micrasterias hardyi*: endemic; NSW, Vic., Tas.

Micrasterias mahabuleshwarensis: cosmopolitan; NT, SA, Qld, NSW, Vic., Tas.

Notes: *Micrasterias* is widespread and common in (at least slightly) acid ponds and lakes.

Compare With: *Staurastrum*.

Caption:
Micrasterias X 250 (top), X 500 (bottom).

MICRASTERIAS

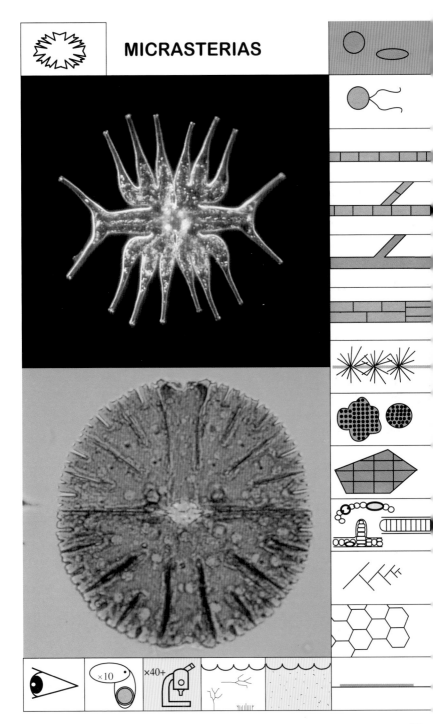

45

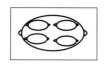 **OOCYSTIS**

Habitat: Free-floating in pools, ditches and lakes; also on soil.

Colour: Green.

Habit: The solitary cells or colonies of 2–16 individuals are enclosed by a persistent and greatly swollen cell from the previous generation.

Microscopic Features: The cells are 20–40 μm long, ovoid to ellipsoid with rounded poles, and the 1–many chloroplasts are irregular or star-shaped, with or without pyrenoids.

Classification: Division Chlorophyta, Family Oocystaceae.

Species and Distribution: c. 44 species, cosmopolitan; 23 species reported from Australia.

e.g. *Oocystis parva*: cosmopolitan; Qld, NSW, Vic., Tas.

Notes: *Oocystis* is widespread and common.

Compare With: None in this guide.

Caption:
Oocystis X 1000 (top), X 900 (middle, bottom-left), X 1000 (bottom-right).

OOCYSTIS

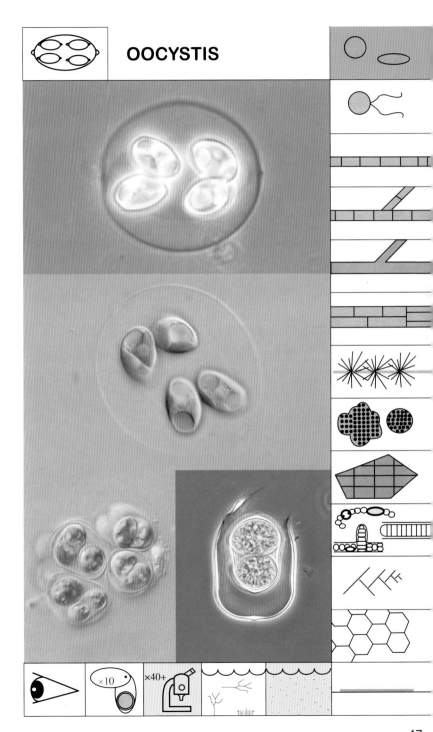

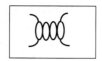

SCENEDESMUS

Habitat: Free-floating in ponds and lakes; also on damp soil.

Colour: Green.

Habit: The flat, generally few-celled colony, includes cells with their long axes parallel to each other.

Microscopic Features: The usually 4–8 (rarely to 16 or more) ovoid, fusiform or crescent-shaped cells lie side by side in a series or in a double row with cells alternating. The terminal cells always have spines, the other cells having smooth walls, spines, teeth or ridges. The cells are 8–20 μm long, uninucleate and have plate-like chloroplasts covering most of the cell wall, with one pyrenoid.

Classification: Division Chlorophyta, Family Scenedesmaceae.

Species and Distribution: 100–150 species, cosmopolitan; 27 species reported from Australia.

e.g. *Scenedesmus obliquus*: cosmopolitan; NT, Qld, NSW, Vic.
       Scenedesmus quadricaudus: cosmopolitan; NT, Qld, NSW, Vic., Tas.

Notes: *Scenedesmus* is common in most standing water. *Scenedesmus bijugus*, sometimes spelt *S. bijugatus,* is now a synonym of *S. obliquus.*

Compare With: None in this guide.

Caption:
Scenedesmus X 1500 (top), X 2000 (middle, bottom-left), X 1000 (bottom).

SCENEDESMUS

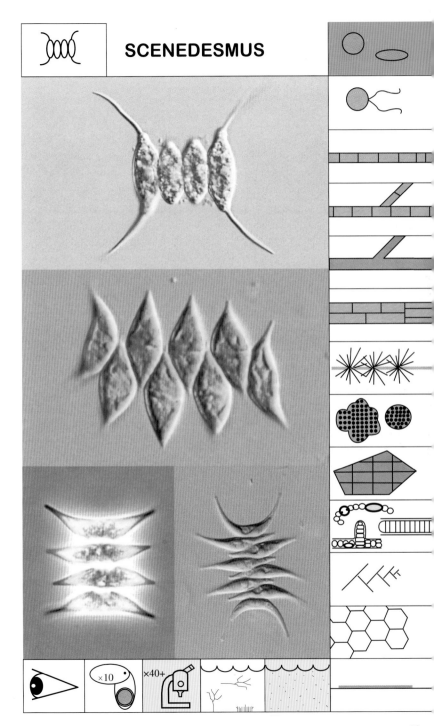

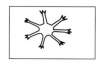

STAURASTRUM

Habitat: Free-floating in lakes.

Colour: Green.

Habit: This desmid is usually radially symmetrical in end view, but may be strongly compressed and bilaterally symmetrical.

Microscopic Features: The cells are 15–90 μm long and divided into two equal portions (semi-cells), with a single chloroplast in each; the central nucleus is prominent. Cell shape and ornamentation vary within the genus but cells are usually triangular in end view and always deeply constricted with an acute-angled sinus.

Classification: Division Chlorophyta, Family Desmidiaceae.

Species and Distribution: 1200 species, cosmopolitan; c. 180 species reported from Australia.

e.g.   *Staurastrum gracile*: cosmopolitan; NT, SA, Qld, NSW, Vic., Tas.

Staurastrum sagittarium: New Zealand, Papua New Guinea, Africa; NT, SA, Qld, NSW, Vic., Tas.

Staurastrum smithii: cosmopolitan; NT, SA, NSW, Vic., Tas.

Notes: *Staurastrum* is widespread and extremely diverse.

Compare With: *Cosmarium, Micrasterias.*

Caption:
Staurastrum X 500 (top), X 600 (middle-left, middle-right), X 800 (bottom-left, bottom-right).

STAURASTRUM

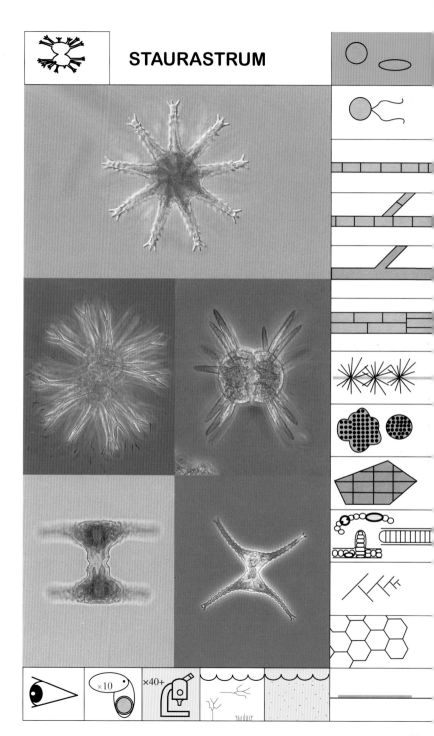

51

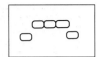

STICHOCOCCUS

Habitat: Damp soils, wood or bark, but sometimes found as an epiphyte on aquatic plants.

Colour: Green.

Habit: The short unbranched filaments are one cell thick.

Microscopic Features: The cylindrical cells have a broadly rounded end and are usually 2–3 μm diameter. The filaments frequently dissociate into single cells. Chloroplasts cover less than half of the transverse wall of the cell and pyrenoids are absent.

Classification: Division Chlorophyta, Family Ulotrichaceae.

Species and Distribution: c. 12 species, cosmopolitan; three species reported from Australia.

e.g.   *Stichococcus bacillaris*: cosmopolitan; Qld, Vic.
          Stichococcus variabilis: cosmopolitan; Vic.

Notes: *Stichococcus* is probably widespread and common, particularly on soil. As with *Klebsormidium*, *Stichococcus* is now classified distant from *Ulothrix*.

Compare With: *Klebsormidium, Microspora, Tribonema.*

Caption:
Stichococcus X 1300 (top-left, bottom-right), X 2000 (middle).

STICHOCOCCUS

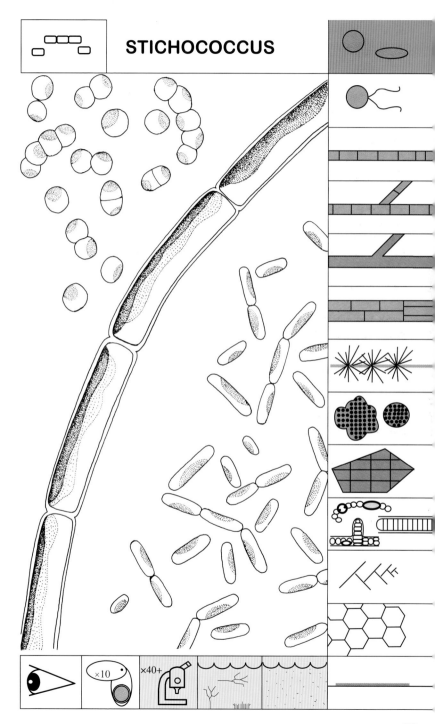

53

TABELLARIA

Habitat: Free-floating in streams, ponds and lakes; sometimes forming macroscopic build-ups among filamentous algae.

Colour: Yellow-brown.

Habit: The elongate cells of this diatom are often attached end-to-end to form a zigzag chain.

Microscopic Features: The cells are c. 40–60 µm long and may be attached asymmetrically at their narrow ends by gelatinous cushions. A gap (pseudoraphe) is evident between the transverse markings. Each cell has numerous minute discoid chloroplasts.

Classification: Division Bacillariophyta, Family Tabillariaceae.

Species and Distribution: Four species, cosmopolitan; all species reported from Australia.

e.g.   *Tabellaria flocculosa*: cosmopolitan; NT, Qld, NSW, Vic., Tas.

Notes: *Tabellaria* is widespread.

Compare With: *Gomphonema, Fragilaria.*

Caption:
Diatom film removed from rocks in stream (top).
Tabellaria X 250 (middle), X 800 (bottom).

TABELLARIA

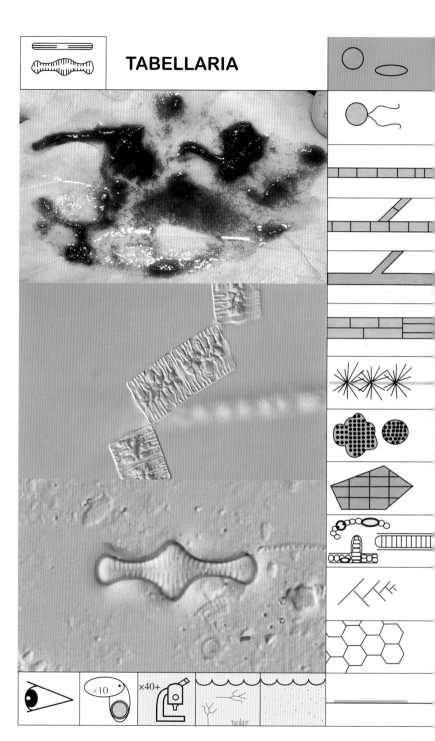

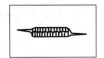

UROSOLENIA

Habitat: Free-floating in lakes and ponds.

Colour: Yellow-brown.

Habit: The tips of this more or less cylindrical diatom taper to a long needle-like point. The cells are 40–200 μm long and sometimes joined together in a straight or spiralled filament.

Microscopic Features: The cell walls produce of a series of bands which interlock to form a zigzag line along the length of the cell. The cells contains numerous discoid chloroplasts.

Classification: Division Bacillariophyta, Family Rhizosoleniaceae.

Species and Distribution: Four or five species, cosmopolitan; three species reported from Australia.

e.g. *Urosolenia eriensis*: cosmopolitan; WA, NT, NSW, Vic., Tas.

Notes: *Urosolenia* is apparently widespread. Previously known as *Rhizosolenia*.

Compare With: *Acanthoceras*.

Caption:
Urosolenia X 500 (top, middle).
Asterionella, another common planktonic diatom, X 300 (bottom).

UROSOLENIA

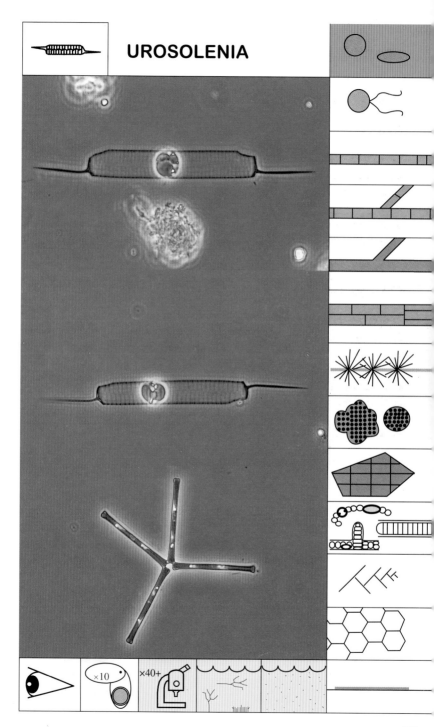

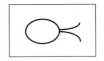

CHLAMYDOMONAS

Habitat: Free-swimming in ponds, lakes and also on snow.

Colour: Green (occasionally forming red blooms).

Habit: Solitary cells which may be spherical, ellipsoidal, subcylindrical or pear-shaped, with two flagella inserted close to each other.

Microscopic Features: The cells are 5–15 μm diameter and contain a single chloroplast (variable form depending on species) with usually one or more pyrenoids, and one to many contractile vacuoles (typically two near the base of the flagella). Cells sometimes shed flagella and form colonies in a gelatinous matrix

Classification: Division Chlorophyta, Family Chlamydomonadaceae.

Species and Distribution: c. 500 species, cosmopolitan; 38 species reported from Australia.

e.g. *Chlamydomonas globosa*: cosmopolitan; Qld, NSW.
Chlamydomonas snowiae: cosmopolitan; Qld, NSW.

Notes: *Chlamydomonas* is a common inhabitant of ponds and lakes. Although there a number of algae that colonize snow, species of *Chlamydomonas* are usually responsible for any pink or red coloration (see page 11). The pinkish colour of saline lakes (see page 19) is generally caused by a bloom of *Dunaliella salina*, an alga similar to *Chlamydomonas* but lacking a firm outer wall. *Haematococcus* is similar to *Chlamydomonas* as it also has two flagella, however the cell contents are contained within a central body connected to the outer wall with fine protoplasmic threads. *Haematococcus* cells are normally green, but as growth conditions become unfavourable, red pigmentation increases. *Haematococcus* is common in garden ponds and bird baths.

Compare With: *Cryptomonas, Euglena, Phacus.*

Caption:
Chlamydomonas X 600 (top), X 2000 (left drawing).
Haematococcus, a similar genus, X 850 (middle), X 600 (right drawing).

CHLAMYDOMONAS

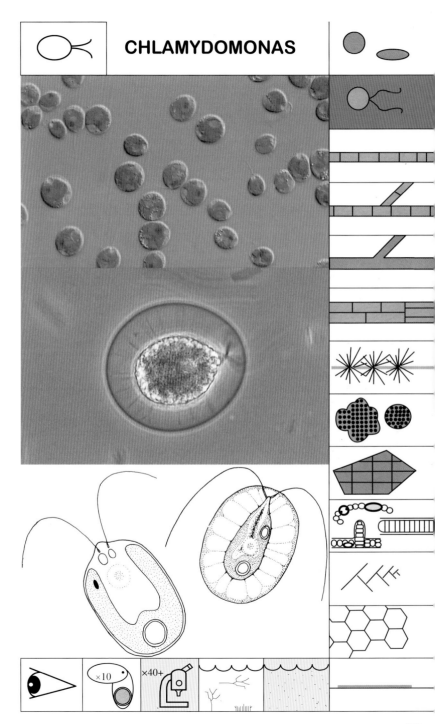

CRYPTOMONAS

Habitat: Free-floating in ponds and lakes.

Colour: Usually olive-brown.

Habit: The asymmetric solitary cells are flattened, with two flagella arising from an anterior gullet.

Microscopic Features: The slipper-shaped cells are 15–50 μm long and have one or two large yellowish to olive green chloroplasts and 1–3 contractile vacuoles.

Classification: Division Cryptophyta, Family Cryptomonadaceae.

Species and Distribution: c. 40 species, cosmopolitan; seven species reported from Australia.

e.g.   *Cryptomonas erosa*: cosmopolitan; Qld, NSW, Tas.

Notes: *Cryptomonas* is reported rarely but it is common in most standing waters. *Chroomonas* is morphologically very similar to *Cryptomonas* but has no gullet and is relatively smaller. Another common cryptomonad, *Chilomonas* is very similar to *Cryptomonas,* but lacks chloroplasts and is found commonly in organic-rich waters.

Compare With: *Chlamydomonas, Euglena, Phacus.*

Caption:
Cryptomonas X 800 (top-left, drawing).
Campylomonas, a similar genus, X 800 (top-right).
Chilomonas, a similar genus, X 1000 (middle-left).
Chroomonas, a similar genus, X 125 (middle-right).

CRYPTOMONAS

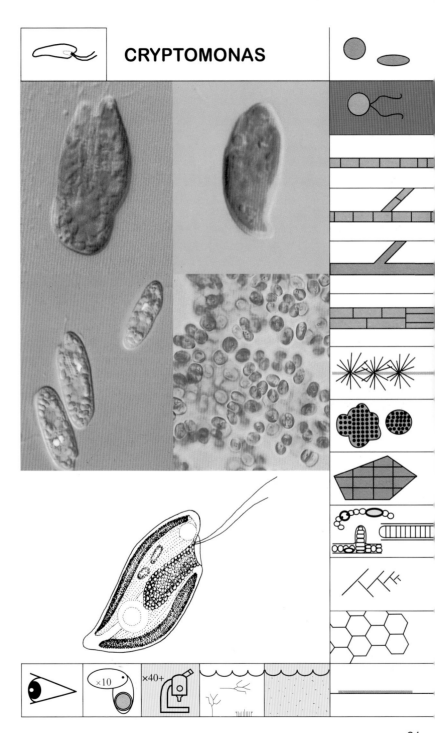

 **EUGLENA**

Habitat: Free-swimming in ponds and lakes; also on organic-rich mud.

Colour: Green (sometimes red).

Habit: The elongate cells have a single flagellum arising from an anterior gullet.

Microscopic Features: The mostly free-swimming cells are 60–125 μm long and continually change shape as they 'creep' through the water. The fusiform, cylindrical to ovate cells have a more or less pointed posterior (end opposite flagella), a gullet and a red eyespot at the anterior end, and one or more contractile vacuoles. The chloroplasts (sometimes absent) are numerous, ovoid, ribbon-like or star-shaped, occasionally with pyrenoids. Rod-shaped structures (paramylon bodies) are visible inside the cells.

Classification: Division Euglenophyta, Family Euglenaceae.

Species and Distribution: c. 152 species, cosmopolitan; 33 species reported from Australia.

e.g.   *Euglena acus*: cosmopolitan; NT, SA, Qld, NSW, Vic., Tas.
Euglena oxyuris: cosmopolitan; NT, Qld, NSW, Vic., Tas.

Notes: *Euglena* is widespread and often abundant, occasionally forming green or red powdery films on the surface of ponds. These films may change from green to red in a few hours.

Compare With: *Chlamydomonas, Cryptomonas, Phacus, Trachelomonas.*

Caption:
Euglena, change in shape associated with 'euglenoid movement' X 400 (top-left, top-right), anterior end of cell in two focal planes X 300 (middle-left, middle-right), X 400 (bottom).

EUGLENA

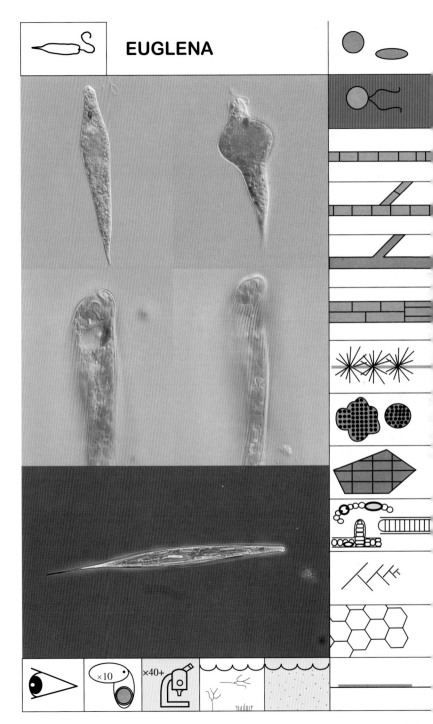

MALLOMONAS

Habitat: Free-swimming in ponds and lakes, frequently among weeds.

Colour: Golden-yellow to light brown.

Habit: Oval or elliptical cells with a single emergent flagellum and an outer covering of overlapping siliceous scales.

Microscopic Features: The cells are 25–60 μm long and contain one or two longitudinal chloroplasts. The siliceous scales are often terminated by highly visible bristles, mostly trailing anteriorly giving the cells a hairy appearance. A second non-emergent flagella is situated within an apical opening.

Classification: Division Chrysophyta, Family Fragilariaceae.

Species and Distribution: c. 80 species, cosmopolitan; 34 species reported from Australia.

e.g.　*Mallomonas splendens*: cosmopolitan; NT, Qld, NSW, Vic., Tas.

Notes: *Mallomonas* is widespread and common; blooms of this species have a characteristic fishy odour.

Compare With: *Dinobryon, Synura.*

Caption:
Mallomonas X 800.

MALLOMONAS

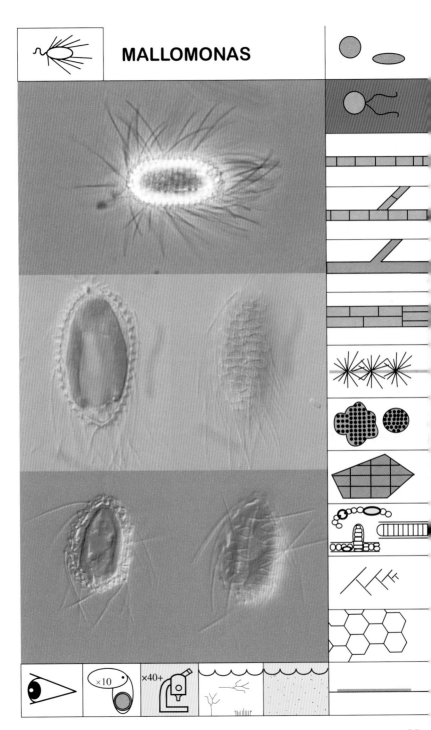

PERIDINIUM

Habitat: Free-swimming in ponds and lakes.

Colour: Yellow-brown to light-brown.

Habit: The cells are more or less globose to top-shaped.

Microscopic Features: The cells are 40–80 μm long and enclosed in a number of thick plates (often with reticulate thickenings) separated by obvious sutures; one end of the cell sometimes bears small spines. A transverse furrow (cingulum) completely encircling the cell, contains one of the two flagella. Each cell has numerous yellowish-brown chloroplasts.

Classification: Division Dinophyta, Family Peridiniaceae.

Species and Distribution: 30 species, cosmopolitan; 29 species reported from Australia.

e.g.   *Peridinium inconspicuum*: cosmopolitan; NT, Qld, NSW.

Notes: *Peridinium* is a widespread and common dinoflagellate (a member of the Division Dinophyta). Some authors treat *P. inconspicuum* as a synonym of a broadly circumscribed *P. umbonatum.* Another common dinoflagellate is *Gymnodinium,* which lacks the covering plates.

Compare With: None in this guide.

Caption:
Peridinium X 570 (top-left, top-right, left drawing), X 500 (middle-left photograph).
Ceratium, another dinoflagellate, X 350 (middle-right photograph).
Gymnodinium, another dinoflagellate, X 400 (bottom-left photograph, bottom-right photograph, right drawing).

PERIDINIUM

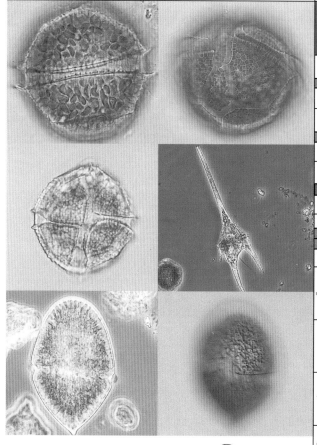

PHACUS

Habitat: Free-swimming in ponds and lakes.

Colour: Green.

Habit: The single cells are more or less flattened and rigid, sometimes twisted posteriorly with a long 'tail-piece' (caudus). A single flagellum arises from an anterior gullet.

Microscopic Features: The cells are 30–140 μm long and have longitudinal striae and small discoid chloroplasts lacking pyrenoids. A single (sometimes 2–3), generally transparent, large ring or doughnut-shaped structure (paramylon body) is located centrally in the cell.

Classification: Division Euglenophyta, Family Euglenaceae.

Species and Distribution: 150 species, cosmopolitan; 33 species reported from Australia.

e.g.   *Phacus longicauda*: cosmopolitan; NT, Qld, NSW, Vic.

        Phacus pleuronectes: cosmopolitan; NT, Qld, NSW, Vic.

        Phacus tortus: cosmopolitan; NT, Qld, NSW, Vic., Tas.

Notes: *Phacus* is widespread and common, typically in nutrient-enriched water. It is similar to *Euglena* but the cells are rigid rather than plastic. *Lepocinclis* is similar to both genera but two very large and conspicuous lateral rings or plates (paramylon bodies).

Compare With: *Chlamydomonas, Cryptomonas , Euglena.*

Caption:
Phacus X 1500 (top), showing doughnut-shaped paramylon body X 650 (middle-left, middle-right), X 600 (bottom-right).

PHACUS

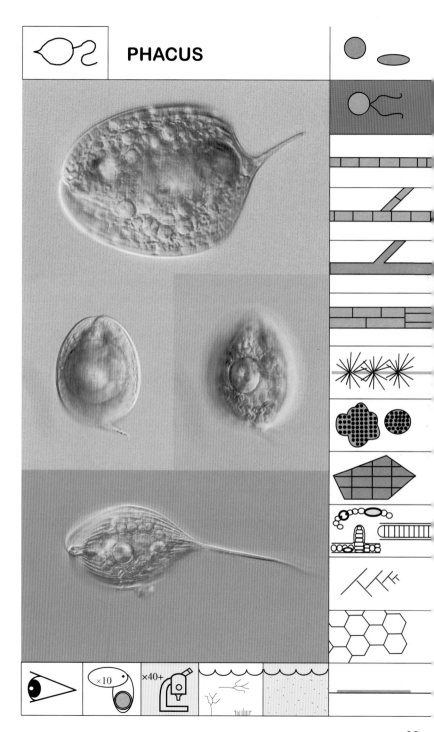

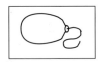

TRACHELOMONAS

Habitat: Free-swimming in shallow ponds or bogs, or among the water plants on lake shores.

Colour: Yellow to dark brown or red.

Habit: The firm brown shell is variously shaped (round, oval or flask-shaped) and ornamented with spines, warts and pits, often with a collar at the aperture through which a single flagellum extends.

Microscopic Features: The cells are 14–60 μm long and enclosed in a rigid shell (lorica) that varies in colour with the impregnation of iron. The numerous ovoid to disc-shaped chloroplasts may have pyrenoids.

Classification: Division Euglenophyta, Family Euglenaceae.

Species and Distribution: c. 250 species, cosmopolitan; 102 species reported from Australia.

e.g. *Trachelomonas armata*: cosmopolitan; NT, Qld, NSW, Vic.

Trachelomonas hispida: cosmopolitan; NT, SA, Qld, NSW, Vic.

Trachelomonas volvocina: cosmopolitan; NT, SA, Qld, NSW, Vic., Tas.

Notes: *Trachelomonas* is widespread and extremely diverse. In large numbers it may colour the water deep red-brown (but not forming a powdery surface film like *Euglena*). *Trachelomonas* is more common where organic material concentrations and temperatures are higher.

Compare With: *Euglena.*

Caption:
Trachelomonas X 850 (top-left), X 600 (top-right), X 750 (middle-left, middle-right), X 1500 (bottom-left), X 1300 (bottom-right).

TRACHELOMONAS

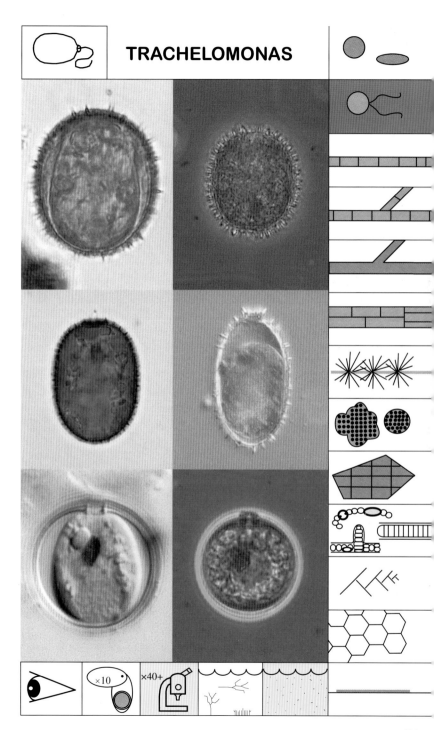

AULACOSEIRA

Habitat: Free-floating or attached to rock and aquatic plants in urban or slightly eutrophic streams, as well as lakes and large slow-flowing rivers (such as the Murray River).

Colour: Brown.

Habit: A cylindrical diatom, sometimes with a pitted surface, forming unbranched filaments.

Microscopic Features: The cells are 4–20 μm diameter and mostly longer than broad; chloroplasts are discoid and numerous. The surface pits are arranged in straight or spiralled rows. Spines are sometimes present on the end walls.

Classification: Division Bacillariophyta, Family Aulacoseiraceae.

Species and Distribution: 20 species, cosmopolitan; 14 species reported from Australia.

e.g.   *Aulacoseira distans*: cosmopolitan; NT, SA, NSW, Vic., Tas.
        Aulacoseira granulata: cosmopolitan; WA, NT, Qld, NSW, Vic., Tas.
        Aulacoseira italica: cosmopolitan; WA, NT, Qld, NSW, Vic., Tas.

Notes: *Aulacoseira* is abundant, forming dark brown strands on many surfaces in urban creeks and large rivers. *Aulacoseira* was previously called *Melosira*: the commonly reported *Melosira varians* remains in that genus.

Compare With: None in this guide.

Caption:
Aulacoseira attached to rocks in a stream (top), X 1000 (upper-middle, lower-middle).
Melosira, as now defined, X 400 (bottom).

AULACOSEIRA

CYLINDROCAPSA

Habitat: Loosely adhering to rocks in streams and stagnant pools.

Colour: Green.

Habit: The short unbranched filaments are a single cell thick and attached to the substrate by holdfasts.

Microscopic Features: The ovoid to quadrate cells are c. 10–25 μm broad with thick stratified cell walls. There is a single stellate chloroplast with a single pyrenoid.

Classification: Division Chlorophyta, Family Cylindrocapsaceae.

Species and Distribution: 2–3 species, cosmopolitan; three species reported from Australia.

e.g.   *Cylindrocapsa geminella*: cosmopolitan; SA, Qld.
       Cylindrocapsa involuta: cosmopolitan; Tas.
       Cylindrocapsa oedogoniales: India; Qld.

Notes: *Cylindrocapsa* has been reported rarely.

Compare With: *Chroodactylon.*

Caption:
Cylindrocapsa X 700 (drawings), X 800 (photograph).

CYLINDROCAPSA

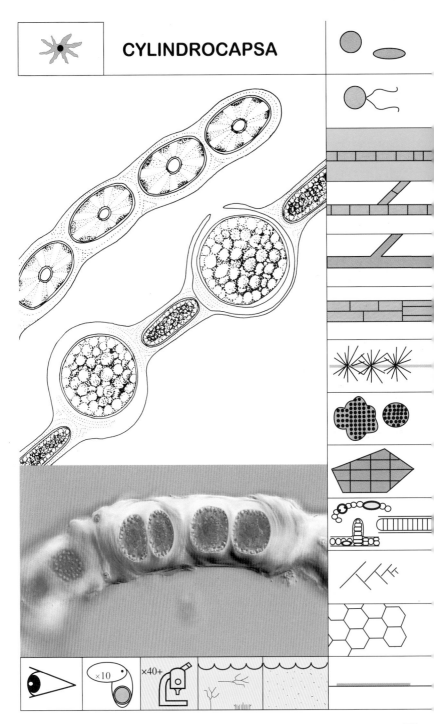

HYALOTHECA

Habitat: Loosely attached in semi-eutrophic, often silty, streams or drains.

Colour: Green.

Habit: This unusual desmid forms unbranched filaments, sometimes with a wide gelatinous sheath.

Microscopic Features: The unbranched chain of cylindrical to discoid cells is 5–15 μm diameter. The cells are divided into two equal portions (semi-cells), with a single star-shaped chloroplast in each; the central nucleus is prominent. Each cell has flattened poles and the surface is sometimes marked with rings of pits.

Classification: Division Chlorophyta, Family Desmidiaceae.

Species and Distribution: 12 species, cosmopolitan; seven species reported from Australia.

e.g.   *Hyalotheca dissiliens*: cosmopolitan; SA, Qld, NSW, Vic., Tas.
Hyalotheca hians: endemic; Qld, NSW.
Hyalotheca mucosa: cosmopolitan; NT, Qld, NSW, Vic.

Notes: *Hyalotheca* is widespread and common.

Compare With: *Aulacoseira.*

Caption:
Hyalotheca X 1000 (top), X 2000 (middle), markings on cell surface X 2000 (bottom).

HYALOTHECA

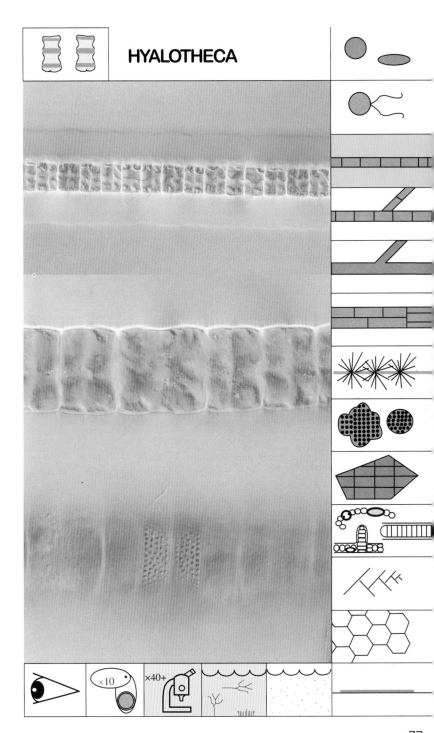

KLEBSORMIDIUM

Habitat: Loosely attached or floating in streams and ponds, or on damp soil. In flowing water it often grows at or above the water surface in cooler months.

Colour: Green.

Habit: The unbranched filaments are a single cell thick and have no distinct attachment cell at maturity (however adhesive pads may form at elbow-like cell junctions).

Microscopic Features: The cylindrical cells are as long or longer than broad, 4–15 μm diameter, with round chloroplasts. The cells have a single nucleus and a chloroplast usually encircling less than half the lateral cell perimeter but extending the length of the cell, with one pyrenoid.

Classification: Division Chlorophyta, Family Klebsormidiaceae.

Species and Distribution: Seven species, cosmopolitan; two species reported from Australia.

e.g. *Klebsormidium flaccidum*: cosmopolitan; Qld, Vic.
Klebsormidium rivulare: cosmopolitan; SA, NSW, Vic.

Notes: *Klebsormidium* is widespread and often abundant. It is superficially like *Ulothrix* but in more recent classifications it has been placed with *Stichococcus* in a different group based on features of the cell division process.

Compare With: *Rhizoclonium, Stichococcus, Ulothrix.*

Caption:
Klebsormidium X 200 (top), X 1500 (middle, bottom).

KLEBSORMIDIUM

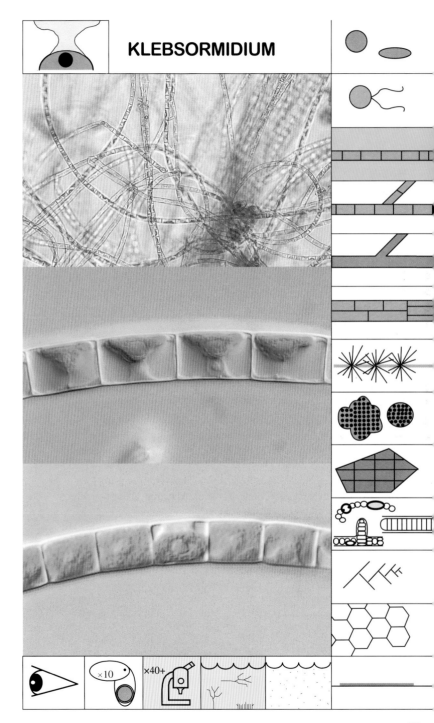

79

MICROSPORA

Habitat: Usually tangled among other filamentous algae in cool, unpolluted streams; found mostly in spring and autumn.

Colour: Green.

Habit: The unbranched filaments are a single cell thick and usually unattached.

Microscopic Features: The cylindrical cells are c. 10–20 μm diameter, with thickened H-shaped cell walls (however the degree of thickening may be environmentally controlled). The chloroplasts are discoid, granular, without a pyrenoid, and arranged in a compact irregular net.

Classification: Division Chlorophyta, Family Microsporaceae.

Species and Distribution: c. 20 species, cosmopolitan; five species reported from Australia.

e.g. *Microspora floccosa*: cosmopolitan; Qld, Vic.
 Microspora pachyderma: cosmopolitan; Qld.
 Microspora tumidula: cosmopolitan; Qld.

Notes: *Microspora* has been reported only occasionally but it is widespread.

Compare With: *Klebsormidium, Stichococcus, Tribonema.*

Caption:
Microspora X 150 (top), X 900 (middle), X 2000 (bottom).

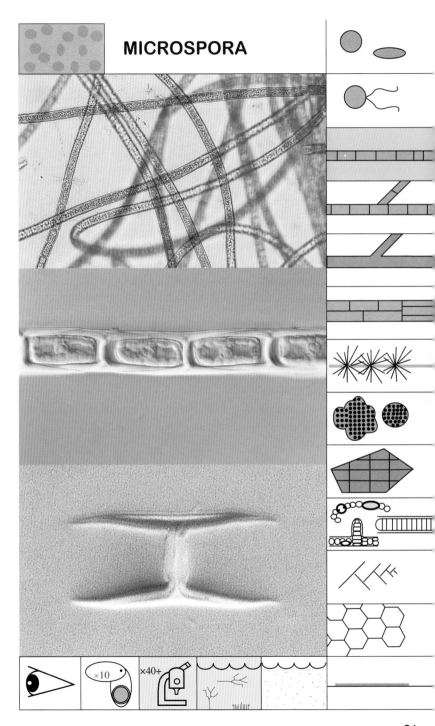

MICROSPORA

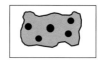

MOUGEOTIA

Habitat: Free floating or attached in lakes, pools, ditches and some streams, often mixed with other green algae.

Colour: Green.

Habit: The unbranched filaments are a single cell thick.

Microscopic Features: The cylindrical cells are 5–55 μm diameter, usually four times as long as broad and with thin walls. There is one (sometimes two) oblong to rectangular chloroplast, able to rotate around the central long-axis of the cell; the chloroplast has two or more large pyrenoids. Sexual reproduction is by conjugation where part of the cytoplasm remains in each of the connecting cells and a new wall forms cutting off the 'gametangia'.

Classification: Division Chlorophyta, Family Zygnemataceae, Subfamily Mougeotioideae.

Species and Distribution: c. 120 species, cosmopolitan; 18 species reported from Australia.

e.g.   *Mougeotia sestertisignifera*: endemic; SA.
          Mougeotia victoriensis: endemic; Vic.
          Mougeotia viridis: cosmopolitan; NSW, Vic.

Notes: *Mougeotia* is widespread and often mixed with other algae. *Debarya* is similar vegetatively but during conjugation the entire contents of each cell form a zygote that is not separated by a wall from the gametangia. Three of the 6–8 described species have been reported from Australia.

Compare With: None in this guide.

Caption:
Mougeotia X 600.

MOUGEOTIA

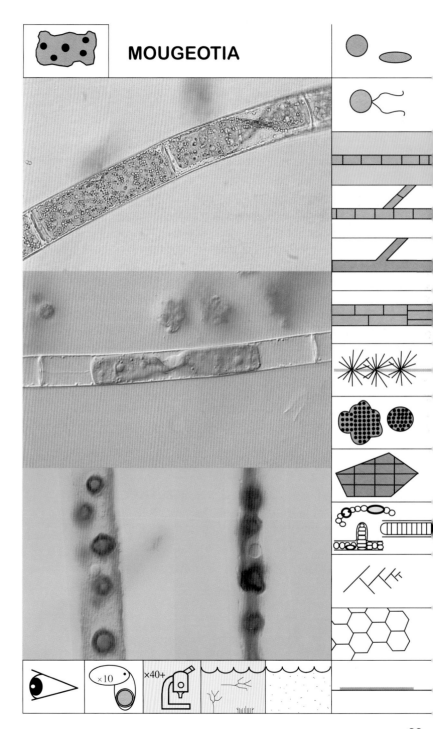

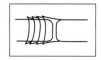

OEDOGONIUM

Habitat: Free floating or attached to rocks in in still or moving water, wood or aquatic plants.

Colour: Green.

Habit: The unbranched, filaments are a single cell thick and often attached by a basal holdfast cell.

Microscopic Features: The cells are 2–90 μm diameter with a single reticulate chloroplast completely encircling the cell and containing several pyrenoids. The remains of the cell walls create distinctive 'rings' at the end of older cells. Sexual reproduction is by fusion of egg and sperm cells, with intercalary female gametangia (usually swollen globular cell) and male gametangia (usually shortened cells similar in thickness to vegetative cells). Male and female gametangia may be born on the same filament or different filaments (sometimes morphologically different as well); sometimes a further minute male generation is produced and becomes epiphytic on the 'mother' filament.

Classification: Division Chlorophyta, Family Oedogoniaceae.

Species and Distribution: c. 400 species, cosmopolitan; c. 70 species from Australia.

e.g.   *Oedogonium capillare*: cosmopolitan; Vic., Tas.
         Oedogonium undulatum: cosmopolitan; NT, Qld, NSW, Vic.
         Oedogonium vesicatum: Europe; WA, Vic.

Notes: *Oedogonium* is readily distinguished from other unbranched, filamentous algae by the 'rings' left after cell division. Note that sometimes a number of cells must be observed to find these rings.

Compare With: *Bulbochaete, Klebsormidium, Rhizoclonium, Ulothrix.*

Caption:
Oedogonium with characteristic 'rings' at end of cell, X 300 (top-left), X 300 (top-right), X 200 (middle-left, middle-right), attached to *Vaucheria* X 100 (bottom-left), young filament with holdfast cell X 200 (bottom-right).

OEDOGONIUM

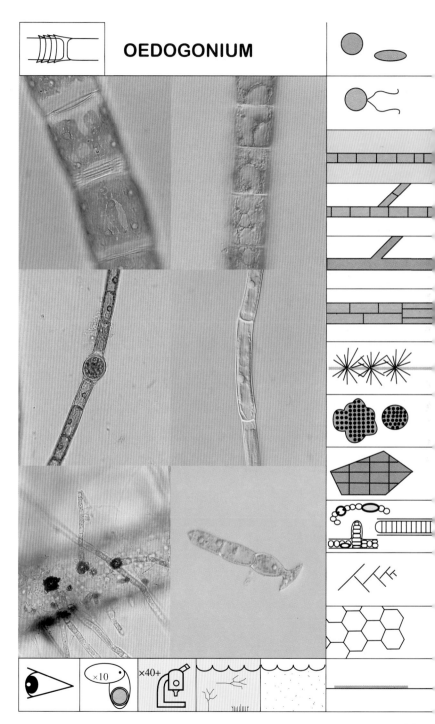

RADIOFILUM

Habitat: Loosely associated with, or attached to, other algae or plants in lakes, swamps and flowing water.

Colour: Green.

Habit: The branched or unbranched filaments are a single cell thick.

Microscopic Features: The spherical or ellipsoid cells are 5–15 μm in diameter and surrounded by a broad gelatinous sheath. The cell wall is in two sections, joined together to form ring-like rim; the chloroplasts are plate-like and with one pyrenoid.

Classification: Division Chlorophyta, Family Ulotrichaceae.

Species and Distribution: 3–4 species, cosmopolitan; three species reported from Australia.

> *Radiofilum conjunctivum*: cosmopolitan; Vic.
> *Radiofilum irregulare*: cosmopolitan; Vic.
> *Radiofilum transversalis*: cosmopolitan; Qld.

Notes: *Radiofilum* is reported rarely.

Compare With: *Chroodactylon.*

Caption:
Radiofilum X 1000 (Y-shape left), X 3500 (right).

RADIOFILUM

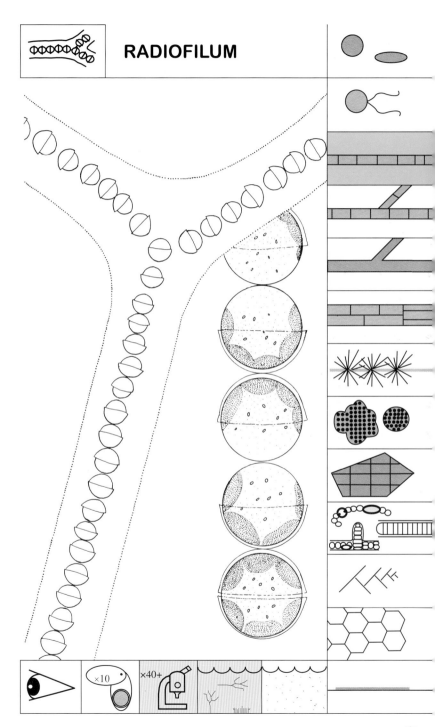

87

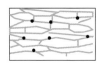

RHIZOCLONIUM

Habitat: Often entangled with other filamentous algae, in slow-flowing water, but sometimes producing extensive, thick mats on its own.

Colour: Green.

Habit: The filaments are one cell thick and unbranched except for occasional rhizoidal filaments of one to a few cells.

Microscopic Features: The thick-walled, cylindrical cells are 10–50 μm diameter and several times longer than broad; the chloroplasts are net-like with many pyrenoids.

Classification: Division Chlorophyta, Family Cladophoraceae.

Species and Distribution: 5–7 species, cosmopolitan; six species reported from Australia.

e.g.   *Rhizoclonium hieroglyphicum*: cosmopolitan; Qld, NSW, Vic., Tas.

Rhizoclonium riparium: cosmopolitan; WA, Qld, NSW (including Lord Howe Island), Vic.

Notes: Generally in alkaline and/or saline streams and common in estuarine areas. *Chaetomorpha* is similar to *Rhizoclonium* but the filaments are more than 70 μm diameter (a seemingly arbitrary generic distinction). *Chaetomorpha linum* has been reported from SA and Vic.

Compare With: *Cladophora, Oedogonium, Ulothrix.*

Caption:
Rhizoclonium attached to rocks emergent from stream (top), X 100 (middle), X 400 (bottom).

RHIZOCLONIUM

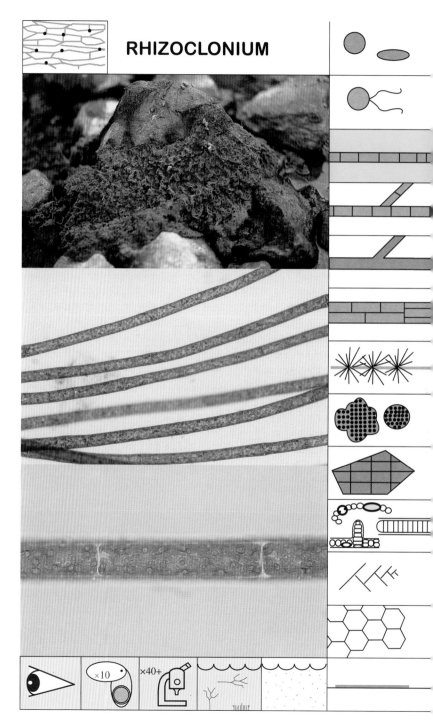

SPHAEROPLEA

Habitat: Floating in stagnant water, flooded pools or gravel pit depressions.

Colour: Green.

Habit: The unbranched filaments are a single cell thick; large red zygotes are sometimes visible.

Microscopic Features: The cylindrical cells are elongate, 25–75 μm diameter, and 15–60 times as long as broad. The outer walls are thin and the cross-walls unevenly thickened. The cytoplasm forms transverse bands between large vacuoles, containing numerous discoid chloroplasts and only some with a pyrenoid, or else band-shaped chloroplasts with several pyrenoids. Sexual reproduction results in a bright red zygote following the fusion of a spherical egg cell and motile male gametes within unmodified vegetative cells.

Classification: Division Chlorophyta, Family Sphaeropleaceae.

Species and Distribution: Seven species, cosmopolitan; one species reported from Australia.

> *Sphaeroplea annulina*: cosmopolitan; NSW, Vic.

Notes: The red zygotes are visible to the naked eye.

Compare With: *Oedogonium.*

Caption:
Sphaeroplea X 350.

SPHAEROPLEA

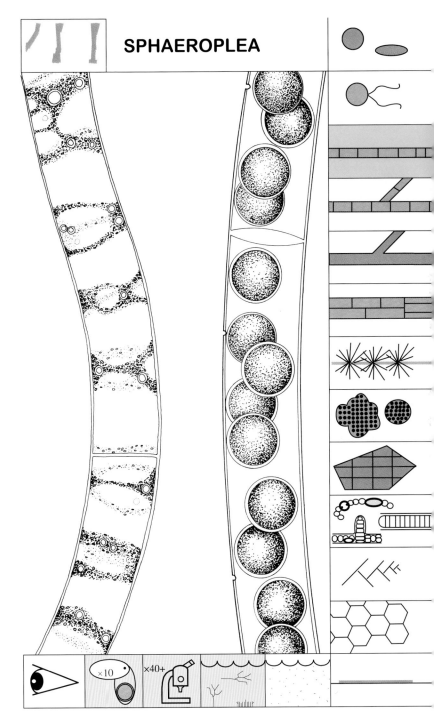

 **SPIROGYRA**

Habitat: Attached or floating in flowing or still water.

Colour: Green.

Habit: The unbranched filaments are one cell thick, and slimy to touch.

Microscopic Features: The cylindrical cells are 20–160 μm diameter and as long as broad or longer. One to several ribbon-shaped chloroplasts spiral longitudinally around the cell; they have numerous, prominent pyrenoids and scalloped margins. Reproduction is by formation of a conjugation tube between adjacent filaments.

Classification: Division Chlorophyta, Family Zygnemataceae, Subfamily Spirogyroideae.

Species and Distribution: c. 300 species, cosmopolitan; 47 species reported from Australia.

e.g.　*Spirogyra columbiana*: cosmopolitan; SA, Qld, Vic.
　　　Spirogyra longata: cosmopolitan; SA, Qld, NSW, Vic.
　　　Spirogyra nitida: cosmopolitan; NT, Qld, NSW, Vic.

Notes: *Spirogyra* sometimes forms extensive mats in ponds and rivers, occasionally blocking channels. *Sirogonium* is similar but has ribbon-like chloroplasts more or less parallel to the long axis of the cell and conjugation by pronounced genuflexion of adjacent filaments without conjugation tubes. *Sirogonium sticticum*, one of 20 species, is occasionally reported from Australia.

Compare With: None in this guide.

Caption:
Spirogyra floating in pond (top-left), X 150 (top-right), two focal planes through the same cell X 500 (middle-left, middle-right), spores in filament X 300 (bottom-left), flanges on cross-wall found in some species X 500 (bottom).

SPIROGYRA

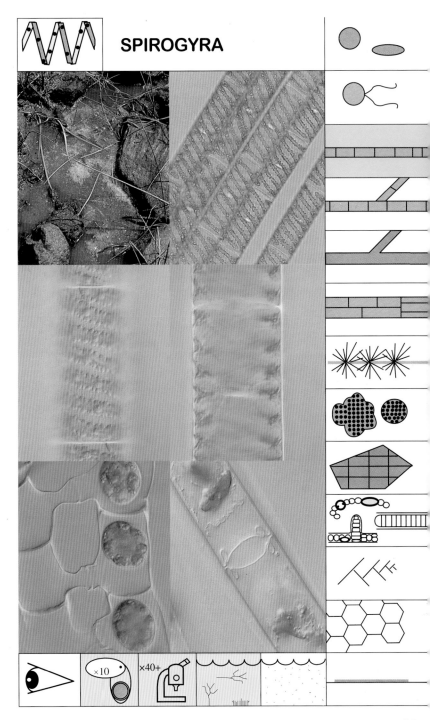

TRIBONEMA

Habitat: Attached to rocks in seepage areas and streams.

Colour: Green to yellow-green.

Habit: The unbranched filaments are one cell thick.

Microscopic Features: The cylindrical to barrel-shaped cells are 3–20 μm diameter and usually more than twice as long as broad. H-shaped cell wall pieces are often visible, particularly when the cells become dissociated. Cells contain one to several yellow-green, discoid (or elongate) chloroplasts without pyrenoids.

Classification: Division Tribophyta, Family Tribonemataceae.

Species and Distribution: 20 species, cosmopolitan; five species reported from Australia.

e.g.   *Tribonema minus*: cosmopolitan; SA, NSW, Vic.

Notes: *Tribonema* is reported rarely but is likely to be widespread.

Compare With: *Microspora*.

Caption:
Tribonema filament and dissociated H-shaped cell wall piece
X 700 (top), X 700 (middle-left), X 900 (middle-right),
X 400 (bottom).

TRIBONEMA

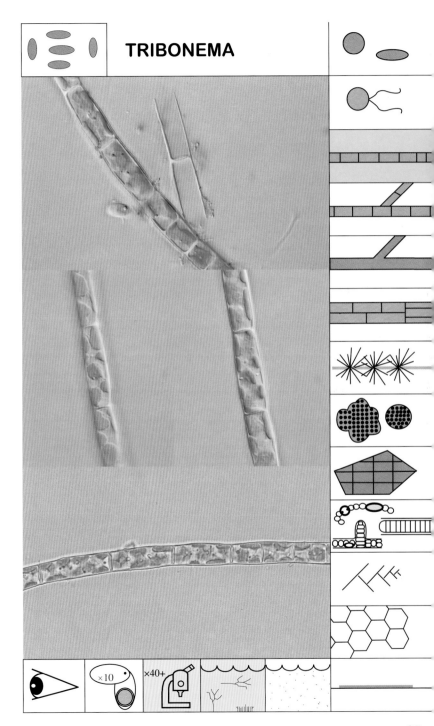

95

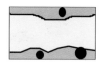

ULOTHRIX

Habitat: Attached in still or flowing water, or on moist rocks near streams or waterfalls.

Colour: Green or yellow-green.

Habit: The unbranched filaments are of indefinite length and attached by specialized cells (at least when young).

Microscopic Features: The cells are 4–40 μm diameter, with lobed or wavy-edged chloroplasts extending for more than half the lateral perimeter of the cell, often with more than one pyrenoid.

Classification: Division Chlorophyta, Family Ulotrichaceae.

Species and Distribution: c. 20 species, cosmopolitan; 16 species reported from Australia.

e.g.   *Ulothrix aequalis*: cosmopolitan; Qld, Vic.

Ulothrix subtilis: cosmopolitan; Qld, NSW, Vic.

Ulothrix zonata: cosmopolitan; Qld, NSW, Vic.

Notes: *Ulothrix* seems to be common in some regions, particularly in rocky streams of Tas.

Compare With: *Klebsormidium, Rhizoclonium, Stichococcus.*

Caption:
Ulothrix attached to concrete in channel (top), X 600 (middle, bottom).

ULOTHRIX

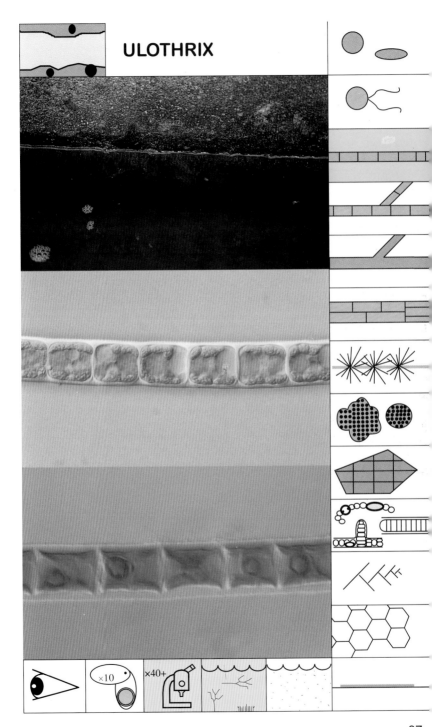

ZYGNEMA

Habitat: Free-floating in still or slow-flowing freshwater habitats.
Colour: Green.

Habit: The unbranched filaments are one cell thick.

Microscopic Features: The cylindrical cells are 8–40 μm diameter and 1–5 times longer than broad. Two star-shaped chloroplasts are found in the middle part of the cell with a nucleus between them. Each chloroplast has a single massive pyrenoid at its centre. Sexual reproduction is by conjugation, where the entire cytoplasm from one cell passes to the other or a zygote forms in the conjugation tube.

Classification: Division Chlorophyta, Family Zygnemataceae, subfamily Zygnemoideae.

Species and Distribution: 120 species, cosmopolitan; 20 species reported from Australia.

e.g.　*Zygnema binuclearioides*: endemic; Qld.
　　　Zygnema cruciatum: cosmopolitan; Qld, NSW, Vic., Tas.

Notes: *Zygnema* is not uncommon but seldom abundant. *Zygnemopsis* has similar vegetative filaments but the zygote (and sexual spores) are surrounded by mucilaginous material. Although including some 40 described species there is only one report of *Zygnemopsis* from Australia. The similar *Zygogonium* is usually terrestrial and can develop into patches up to several metres diameter on soil. It differs from *Zygnema* in having usually thicker walls and often pillow-shaped or globose chloroplasts (only sometimes with radiating processes like those of *Zygnema*).

Compare With: *Cylindrocapsa.*

Caption:
Zygnema X 1000 (top), X 700 (middle), X 400 (bottom).

ZYGNEMA

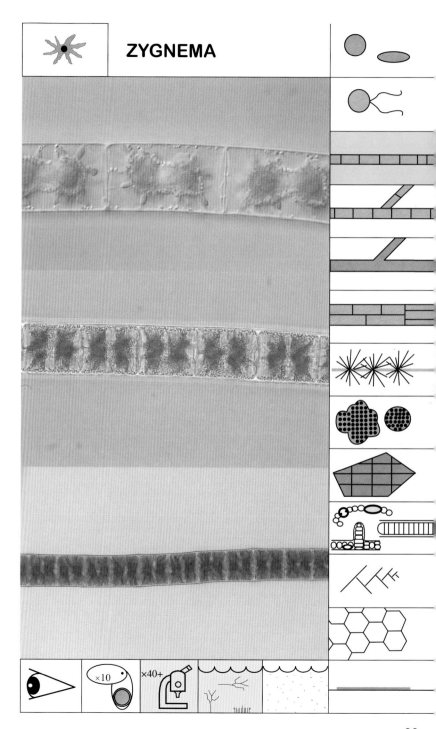

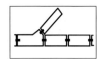

AUDOUINELLA

Habitat: Attached to rocks, roots and aquatic plants in small streams and rivers, in semi-urban to natural areas. Common in autumn.

Colour: Olive-green to grey-brown or red.

Habit: The tufts of freely branched filaments are mostly less than 1 cm long, but larger mats are sometimes produced in still water.

Microscopic Features: The single row of cylindric cells is 5–20 μm diameter with apparent connections between all cells (pit connections). Hairs are sometimes present. The chloroplasts are ribbon-like or plate-like. Asexual reproduction is by terminal rounded spores.

Classification: Division Rhodophyta, Family Acrochaetiaceae.

Species and Distribution: 6–8 species, cosmopolitan; four species reported from Australia.

e.g.   *Audouinella hermannii*: cosmopolitan; SA, Qld, NSW, Vic.

Notes: *Audouinella* is widespread. It is morphologically indistinguishable from the cushion stage of the *Batrachospermum* life history.

Compare With: *Cladophora.*

Caption:
Audouinella attached to rock removed from stream (top),
X 700 (middle), X 300 (bottom).

AUDOUINELLA

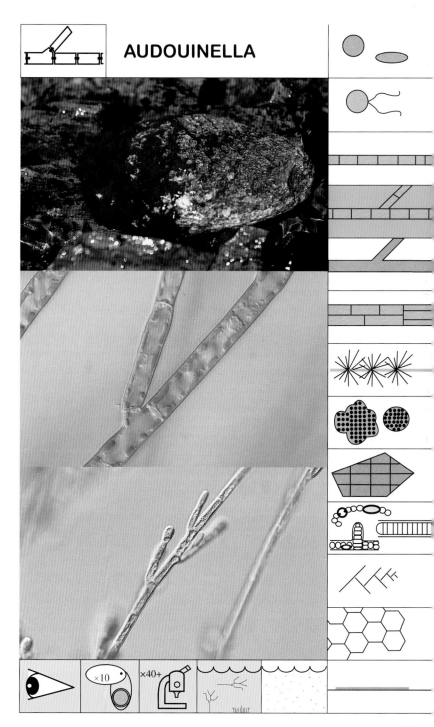

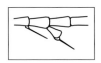

BULBOCHAETE

Habitat: Attached to stones, plants and algae in small permanent bodies of water and streams.

Colour: Green.

Habit: The profusely branched filaments are one cell thick, most cells bearing a long bristle swollen at the base.

Microscopic Features: The cells are 10–25 μm diameter and broader at their upper end, the terminal cell usually with distinctive 'rings' around its base. The chloroplast is reticulate and contains a number of pyrenoids.

Classification: Division Chlorophyta, Family Oedogoniaceae.

Species and Distribution: c. 28 species, cosmopolitan; c. 14 species reported from Australia.

e.g. *Bulbochaete elatior*: cosmopolitan; NT, Qld, NSW.
      Bulbochaete pygmaea: cosmopolitan; Qld, Vic.
      Bulbochaete setigera: cosmopolitan; Qld, NSW, Vic.

Notes: *Bulbochaete* is widespread and presumably common.

Compare With: *Oedogonium, Coleochaete.*

Caption:
Bulbochaete X 100 (top), X 500 (bottom).

BULBOCHAETE

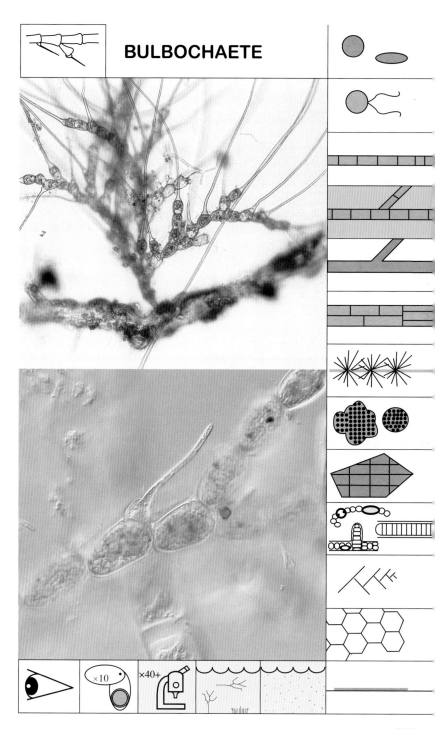

103

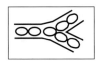

CHROODACTYLON

Habitat: Attached to rocks or other algae in pristine streams.

Colour: Blue-green to black.

Habit: The short filaments form glistening colonies up to 1 mm diameter, or sometimes large mats.

Microscopic Features: The cells, arranged in a single row in an occasionally branched filament are more or less ellipsoid, 3–5 μm diameter, and coated in a thick mucilaginous sheath. The chloroplast is star-shaped, with a single large pyrenoid at its centre.

Classification: Division Rhodophyta, Family Porphyridaceae.

Species and Distribution: One species, cosmopolitan.

    Chroodactylon ornatum: Vic.

Notes: *Chroodactylon* is found in marine and freshwater, and although reported rarely from freshwater it is easily over-looked. In bulk it can be easily mistaken for tufts of Cyanobacteria. *Chroodactylon* was previously called *Asterocytis*.

Compare With: *Cylindrocapsa, Radiofilum.*

Caption:
Chroodactylon X 250 (top), X 600 (middle), X 2000 (bottom).

CHROODACTYLON

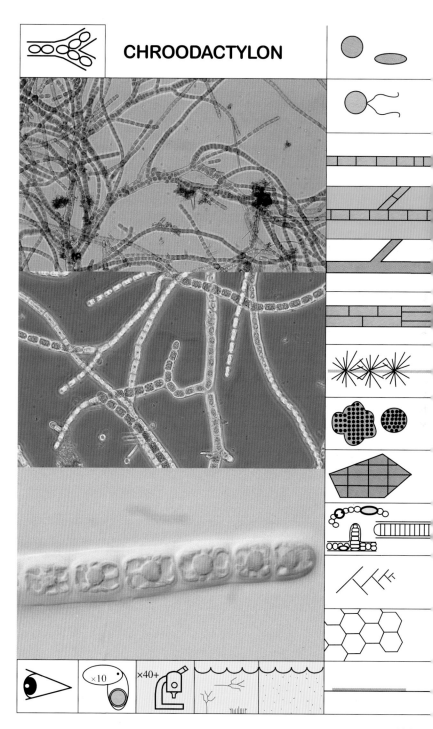

105

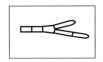

CLADOPHORA

Habitat: Attached to rocks, hard substrates, plants and algae in eutrophic and alkaline streams and lakes.

Colour: Green.

Habit: The filaments are a single cell thick, sparsely to profusely branched, and form tufts or dense mats. They are coarse (not slimy) to touch and attached by rhizoidal cells.

Microscopic Features: The large cylindrical cells are 80–90 μm long and 25–80 μm diameter, with many nuclei, and thick stratified walls. The discoid chloroplasts, some with pyrenoids, usually connect to form a net or closed layer.

Classification: Division Chlorophyta, Family Cladophoraceae.

Species and Distribution: c. 30 species, cosmopolitan; 13 species reported from Australia.

e.g.   *Cladophora aegagropila*: Europe; SA, Vic.

Cladophora fracta: cosmopolitan; Qld.

Cladophora glomerata: cosmopolitan; WA, SA, Qld, NSW, Vic.

Notes: In temperate streams. *Cladophora* is more abundant in warmer months and can form enormous trailing mats to a metre or more in length. It is the major algal weed of urban creeks, and also occurs in enriched ocean bays and harbours.

Compare With: *Pithophora, Rhizoclonium.*

Captions:
Cladophora, extensive mats in urban creek (top), removed from stream (middle), X 100 (bottom-left), X 250 (bottom).

CLADOPHORA

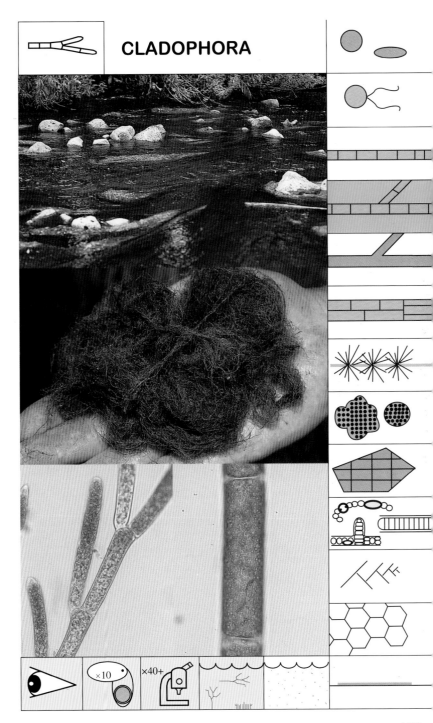

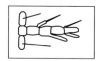

COLEOCHAETE

Habitat: Attached mostly on large aquatic plants.

Colour: Green.

Habit: A generally microscopic alga sometimes with a prostrate disc, or macroscopic producing *Chaetophora*-like colonies.

Microscopic Features: The branched filaments may arise from a prostrate disc of compact cells with protruding, elongate hair-like processes. Cells are 15–50 *μ*m diameter with a single plate-like chloroplast and one large pyrenoid. Sexual reproduction involves a large egg and smaller motile male cells.

Classification: Division Chlorophyta, Family Coleochaetaceae.

Species and Distribution: c .12 species, cosmopolitan; ten species reported from Australia.

e.g.   *Coleochaete divergens*: cosmopolitan; Qld.
   Coleochaete irregularis: cosmopolitan; NT, SA, Qld, NSW, Vic.
   Coleochaete orbicularis: cosmopolitan; Qld, NSW.

Compare With: *Bulbochaete, Chaetophora.*

Caption:
Coleochaete X 450 (drawings), X 150 (photograph).

COLEOCHAETE

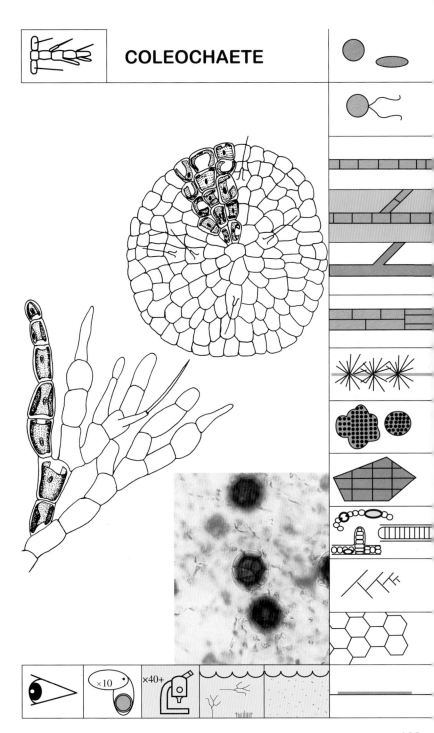

DINOBRYON

Habitat: Free-swimming or attached in pools and lakès.

Colour: Yellowish-brown.

Habit: The cells occupy a 'forked chain of inserted vases'.

Microscopic Features: The biflagellate cells are 30–50 μm long and attached to the inside wall of a cylindrical, vase-like case (lorica) by a narrow cytoplasmic strand. Each cell has an eyespot and one or two chloroplasts.

Classification: Division Chrysophyta, Family Dinobryaceae.

Species and Distribution: 25 species, cosmopolitan; nine species reported from Australia.

e.g.   *Dinobryon cylindricum*: cosmopolitan; NT, Qld, NSW, Vic., Tas.
       Dinobryon divergens: cosmopolitan; NT, Qld, Vic., Tas.
       Dinobryon sertularia: cosmopolitan; NT, Qld, NSW, Vic., Tas.

Notes: *Dinobryon* is widespread and sometimes abundant in polluted waters; in large numbers it may produce a fishy odour. *Dinobryon sertularia* is sometimes called *Poteriodendron petiolatum* var. *abottii*.

Compare With: None in this guide.

Caption:
Dinobryon X 500.

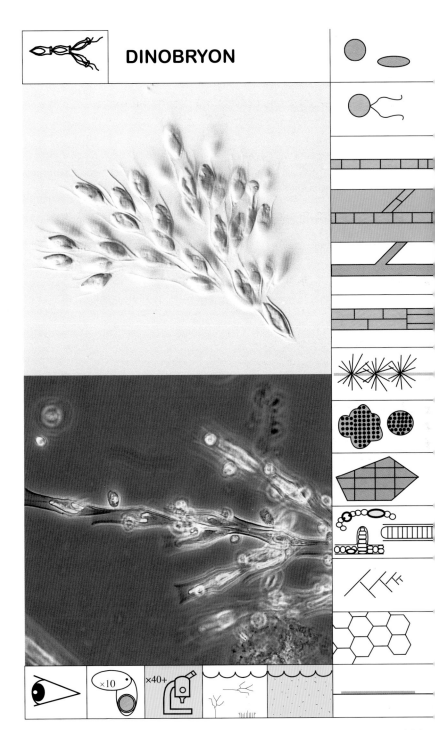

DINOBRYON

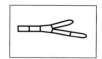

ECTOCARPUS

Habitat: Attached between cracks in basalt rock atop a waterfall.

Colour: Brown.

Habit: The irregularly branched filaments are a single cell thick and may taper gradually to a hair-like cell.

Microscopic Features: The cells are 15–40 μm diameter and contain several elongate lobed chloroplasts each with several pyrenoids. Reproduction is by multicellular sporangia scattered on the branches.

Classification: Division Phaeophyta, Family Ectocarpaceae.

Species and Distribution: One species reported from freshwater.

Ectocarpus siliculosus: cosmopolitan; Vic. (freshwater).

Notes: *Ectocarpus* is known from one locality in western Vic. This is the only record of a brown alga growing in freshwater in the Southern Hemisphere. It is also the only known occurrence of *Ectocarpus* from freshwater anywhere in the world.

Compare With: *Cladophora.*

Caption:
Ectocarpus X 300 (top), X 600 (middle), X 500 (bottom).

ECTOCARPUS

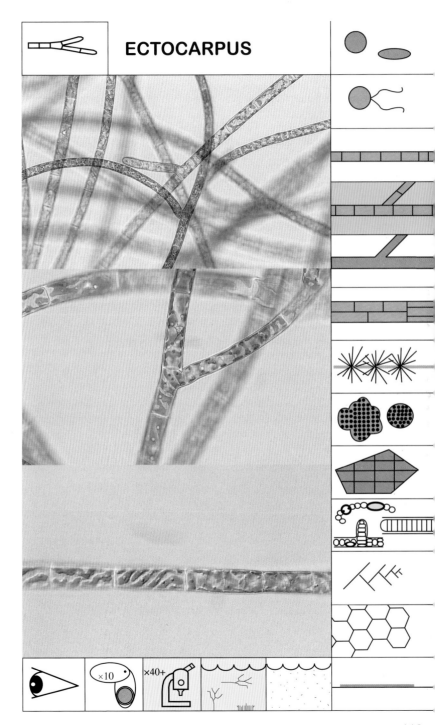

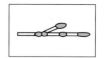

PITHOPHORA

Habitat: Free-floating in pools and lakes, mostly in tropical regions.

Colour: Green.

Habit: The tangled mats of freely branched filaments have large terminal and intercalary akinetes.

Microscopic Features: The large cylindrical cells are 50–100 μm diameter, with many nuclei and thick stratified walls, without lamellation. The discoid chloroplasts, some with pyrenoids, connect to form a net or closed layer. The akinetes are large and alternate with vegetative cells.

Classification: Division Chlorophyta, Family Cladophoraceae.

Species and Distribution: c. 20 species, cosmopolitan; one species reported from Australia.

Pithophora oedogonia: North America, Africa; WA, Qld, ?NSW, Tas.

Notes: *Pithophora* is currently known from only a few disjunct occurrences but it can be a weed of lakes and warm water aquaria. The Tas. record is from hot springs.

Compare With: *Cladophora.*

Caption:
Pithophora X 100 (photograph), X 25 (middle drawing),
X 150 (bottom drawing).

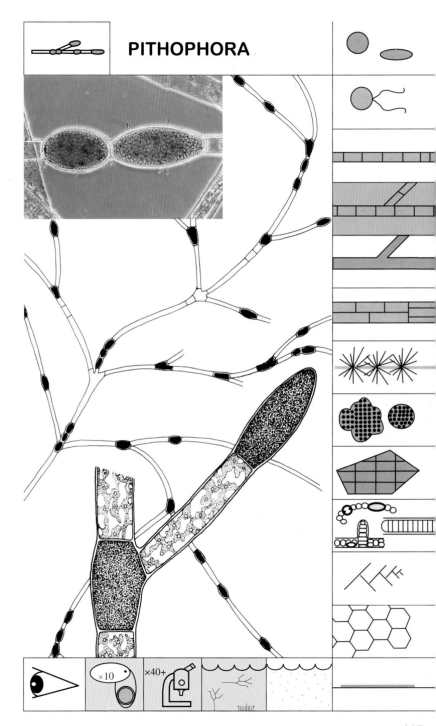

PITHOPHORA

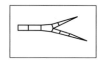

STIGEOCLONIUM

Habitat: Attached to rocks, leaves, stems or rubbish in lakes, mountain and lowland streams, and urban creeks (but only forming extensive growths in the latter).

Colour: Bright green.

Habit: Irregularly branched prostrate filaments closely adhering to the substrate produce a macroscopically visible system of erect filaments.

Microscopic Features: The filaments are mostly one cell thick, 3–10 μm diameter, and the cells have one to several chloroplasts. The erect branched filament have tapering terminal cells with long multicellular hairs.

Classification: Division Chlorophyta, Family Chaetophoraceae.

Species and Distribution: c. 20 species, cosmopolitan; 12 species reported from Australia.

e.g.   *Stigeoclonium tenue*: cosmopolitan; SA, Qld, Vic., Tas.

Notes: *Stigeoclonium* is a common weed species in urban creeks, particularly in winter and spring, but it does not produce the massive clogging growths of *Cladophora*. *Stigeoclonium* grows in a wide range of streams, but usually in fast flowing water. The filaments are more slimy to touch than *Cladophora* but less so than *Spirogyra*.

Compare With: *Chaetophora, Draparnaldia, Ulothrix.*

Caption:
Stigeoclonium attached to rocks in stream (top), X 10 (middle-left), X 400 (middle-right), X 1200 (bottom-left), X 2000 (bottom-right).

STIGEOCLONIUM

BOTRYDIUM

Habitat: Mostly emergent through damp soil, but sometimes submerged.

Colour: Green.

Habit: This unicellular alga consists of a spherical aerial portion 1–2 mm diameter, and a colourless branched rhizoidal portion. The surface of the spherical portion is sometimes coated with calcium carbonate.

Microscopic Features: The multinucleate cell includes a thin peripheral layer of protoplasm with discoid chloroplasts.

Classification: Division Tribophyta, Family Botrydiaceae.

Species and Distribution: 5–6 species, cosmopolitan; two species reported from Australia.

> *Botrydium granulatum*: cosmopolitan; Qld, NSW, Vic.
> *Botrydium wallrothii*: cosmopolitan; Qld.

Notes: *Botrydium* is reported only occasionally but is presumably widespread.

Compare With: *Vaucheria*.

Caption:
Botrydium protruding through soil X 6 (photograph), X 12 (drawing).

BOTRYDIUM

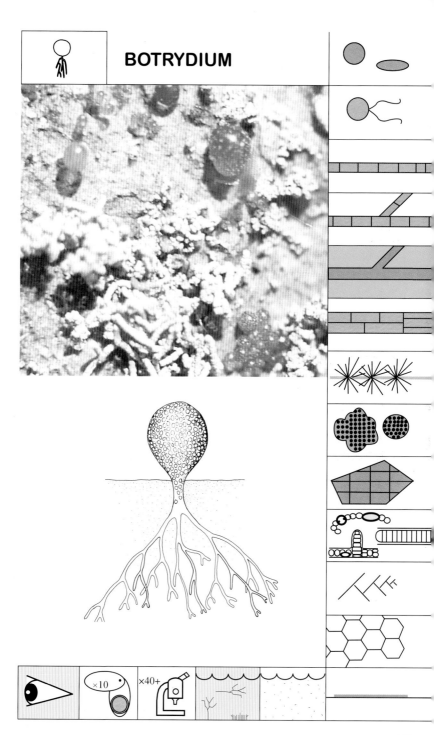

DICHOTOMOSIPHON

Habitat: Attached in shallow pools (but reported overseas to c. 15 m below water level in lakes).

Colour: Green.

Habit: The thallus is siphonous, 50–100 μm diameter, dichotomously branched and regularly constricted.

Microscopic Features: The siphon contains many lens-shaped chloroplasts without pyrenoids or starch. Sexual reproduction is by fusion of sperm and a large spherical egg; asexual reproduction is by thick-walled akinetes.

Classification: Division Chlorophyta, Family Dichotomosiphonaceae.

Species and Distribution: One species, cosmopolitan.

Dichotomosiphon tuberosus: Qld, NSW.

Notes: *Dichotomosiphon* has been collected only twice in Australia, but is possibly more widespread.

Compare With: *Vaucheria.*

Caption:
Dichotomosiphon X 70 (top), X 90 (bottom).

DICHOTOMOSIPHON

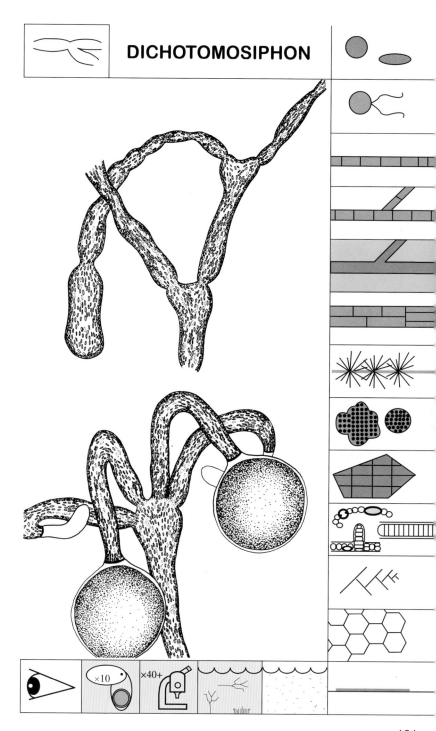

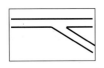

VAUCHERIA

Habitat: Attached to soil in and around streams, lakes and pools; also grows on damp soil.

Colour: Green.

Habit: A tufty mat of tubular branching filaments.

Microscopic Features: There are no cross-walls in the vegetative filament, which is 10–200 μm diameter and contains discoid chloroplasts, usually without pyrenoids. Sexual reproduction is by the fusion of sperm and a large egg; asexual reproduction is by thick-walled akinetes or large zoospore complexes.

Classification: Division Tribophyta, Family Vaucheriaceae.

Species and Distribution: c. 60 species, cosmopolitan; 22 species reported from non-marine habitats in Australia.

e.g. *Vaucheria bursata*: cosmopolitan; SA, Qld, NSW, Vic.

Vaucheria geminata: cosmopolitan; SA, Qld, NSW, Vic.

Vaucheria prona: cosmopolitan; SA, NSW, Vic.

Notes: *Vaucheria* is common and widespread on soil and occasionally abundant in flowing water.

Compare With: *Botrydium, Dichotomosiphon.*

Caption:
Vaucheria growing on moist soil (top), X 200 (middle), chloroplasts X 300 (bottom-left), X 40 (bottom-right).

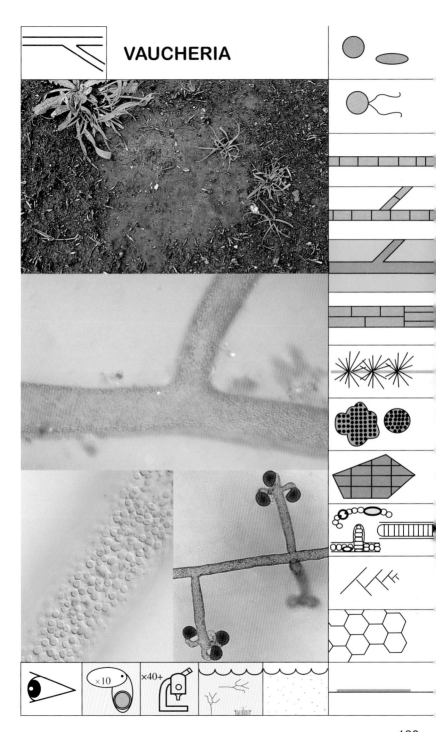

VAUCHERIA

BOSTRYCHIA

Habitat: Attached to rocks in relatively fast-flowing streams.

Colour: Red to brown.

Habit: The erect branching filaments usually have curved or hooked tips.

Microscopic Features: The cylindrical thalli are 100–180 μm diameter and have brick-like tiers of cells closely corticating each cell of the central axis.

Classification: Division Rhodophyta, Family Rhodomelaceae.

Species and Distribution: One species widely reported from freshwater worldwide.

> *Bostrychia harveyi*: Vic., Tas.

Notes: *Bostrychia* is sporadic and is usually found in coastal streams (but well clear of saline waters: e.g. atop waterfalls). *Bostrychia harveyi* was previously reported as *B. scorpioides*.

Compare With: The fine roots or rhizoids of some vascular plants.

Caption:
Bostrychia stained X 80 (top), stained X 120 (middle), X 80 (bottom).

BOSTRYCHIA

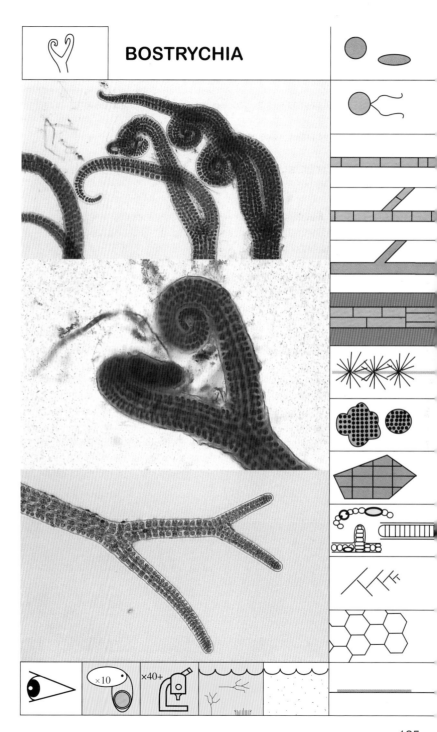

125

COMPSOPOGON

Habitat: Free-floating or attached in eutrophic streams and lakes.

Colour: Olive-green, blue-green or blue-violet.

Habit: The branched filaments eventually becoming a hollow cylinder, 15–40 cm long, 0.1–3 mm wide.

Microscopic Features: The older axes have one or more rows of compact cells around large, colourless axial cells, while the younger filaments have a single row of cells c. 10–50 μm diameter.

Classification: Division Rhodophyta, Family Compsopogonaceae.

Species and Distribution: Six species, cosmopolitan (but mostly tropical and subtropical); one species from Australia.

> *Compsopogon coeruleus*: cosmopolitan; WA, SA, Qld, NSW, Vic.

Notes: *Compsopogon* is a potential nuisance weed and possibly not a genus native to Australia (although reported in Qld as early as 1892). It is widespread and occasionally abundant during warmer months.

Compare With: *Cladophora.*

Caption:
Compsopogon X 60 (top), stained filament in two focal planes X 300 (middle-left, middle-right), stained X 90 (bottom).

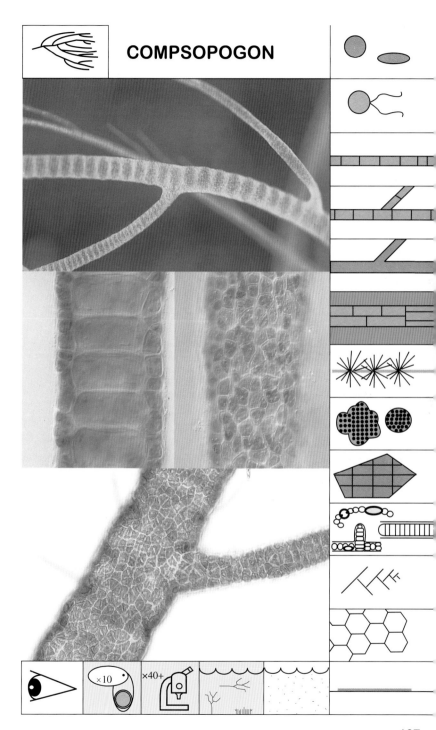

COMPSOPOGON

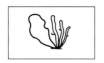

ENTEROMORPHA

Habitat: Attached or free-floating in saline and freshwater lakes and slow-flowing streams.

Colour: Green.

Habit: The alga is tubular (and hollow) when mature, from 2 mm to 2 cm diameter.

Microscopic Features: The angular cells are 8–20 μm diameter and compactly arranged in the single outer layer of the tubular thallus. Each cell has a cup-shaped or plate-like chloroplast usually with one pyrenoid.

Classification: Division Chlorophyta, Family Ulvaceae.

Species and Distribution: 4–7 species, cosmopolitan; seven species reported from inland localities from Australia.

e.g.　*Enteromorpha clathrata*: cosmopolitan; SA, Qld.
　　　Enteromorpha flexuosa: ?cosmopolitan; Qld.
　　　Enteromorpha intestinalis: cosmopolitan; Qld, Vic.
　　　Enteromorpha aff. *prolifera*: cosmopolitan; SA, Vic.

Notes: *Enteromorpha* is reported occasionally from freshwater and sometimes clogs streams. Long trailing filaments may be up to 1.5 m long.

Compare With: *Monostroma.*

Caption:
Enteromorpha through surface of stream (top-left), removed from stream (top-right), X 100 (middle-left, bottom), X 200 (middle-right).

ENTEROMORPHA

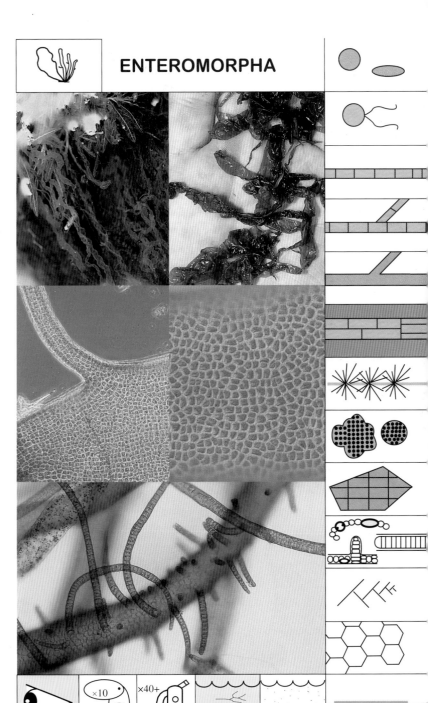

PSILOSIPHON

Habitat: Attached to rocks in or near waterfalls of various heights, in humic-water streams.

Colour: Olive-green to black.

Habit: The firm, erect, fusiform tubes are 1–20 cm long, 0.5–1.5 mm diameter, and little branched. Plants grow in clumps of some 10–30 tubes.

Microscopic Features: The alga has profuse longitudinal medullary filaments and a compact outer cortex.

Classification: Division Rhodophyta, Family Psilosiphonaceae.

Species and Distribution: One species.

Psilosiphon scoparium: New Zealand, NSW, Tas.

Notes: *Psilosiphon* is locally abundant but sporadic; known from only one mainland locality and a handful of sites in south-west Tas.

Compare With: *Batrachospermum.*

Caption:
Psilosiphon attached to rocks near stream (top), X 0.3 (middle), actual size (bottom-left), X 2 (bottom-right).

PSILOSIPHON

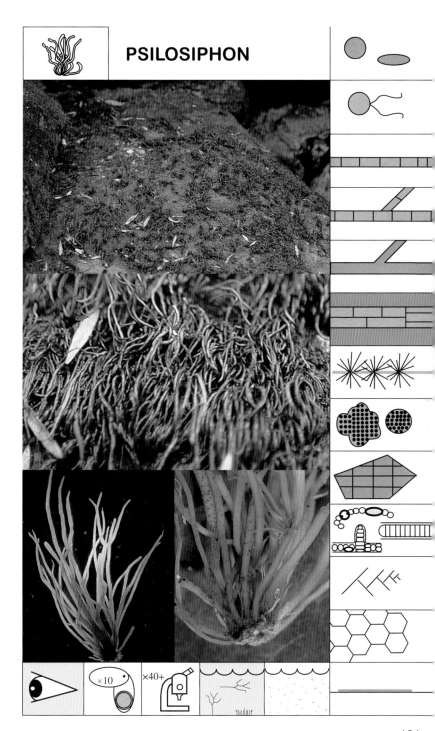

131

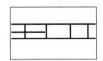

SCHIZOMERIS

Habitat: Free-floating and mixed with other algae in eutrophic running water.

Colour: Green.

Habit: The unbranched (or rarely branched) cylinder of brick-like cells tapers to a single row of elongate cells at the base and a discoid holdfast.

Microscopic Features: The thallus becomes an irregular cylinder, 20–150 μm diameter, with ring-like transverse walls (remnants of the 'single cell thick' phase). A sheet-like chloroplast, with several pyrenoids, wraps around about two-thirds of the cell, becoming more massive in the cylindrical part of the thallus.

Classification: Division Chlorophyta, Family Schizomeridaceae.

Species and Distribution: Two species, cosmopolitan; one species reported from Australia.

> *Schizomeris leibleinii*: cosmopolitan; Qld, NSW, Vic.

Notes: *Schizomeris* is apparently uncommon, but likely to be more widespread than records indicate. Although superficially similar to *Ulothrix,* it is now considered to be more closely allied to the Chaetophoraceae.

Compare With: *Ulothrix.*

Caption:
Schizomeris X 100 (top, bottom), X 250 (middle).

SCHIZOMERIS

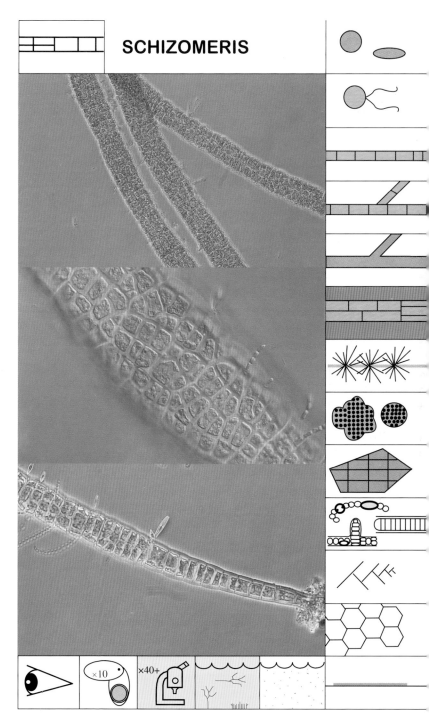

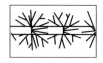

BATRACHOSPERMUM

Habitat: Attached to rocks or wood in cold, pristine streams; occasionally in lakes.

Colour: Red, brown or olive-green (rarely grass-green).

Habit: The stout, gelatinous thallus, 1–10 cm high and up to 2 mm wide, has a prominent central axis surrounded by regular whorls of branchlets often giving it a moniliform appearance. Many species are extremely slimy and will slip from the hand when collected.

Microscopic Features: The cells of the lateral branches contain several discoid or elongate chloroplasts and each contains a pyrenoid. Sexual reproduction is by fusion of non-motile male gametes and specialized female gametes (with an elongate receptor), resulting in large globular or diffuse fruiting clusters within the whorls. Spores from these clusters give rise to a tufted cushion identical to *Audouinella*. An anterior cell of one of these filaments converts to the whorled phase.

Classification: Division Rhodophyta, Family Batrachospermaceae.

Species and Distribution: c. 100 species, cosmopolitan; c. 20 species from Australia.

e.g.　*Batrachospermum atrum*: cosmopolitan; SA, Qld, NSW, Vic., Tas.
　　　Batrachospermum gelatinosum: cosmopolitan; NT, Qld, NSW, Vic.
　　　Batrachospermum nodosum: endemic: Vic.

Notes: *Batrachospermum* is widespread, mostly in mountainous areas. It is sometimes split into a few genera, including in Australia the Southern Hemisphere *Nothocladus* (including *Nothocladus nodosus*) and the cosmopolitan *Sirodotia*.

Compare With: *Draparnaldia*.

Caption:
Batrachospermum attached to rock in stream (top-left), removed from stream X 0.6 (top-right), X 50 (middle), X 100 (bottom).

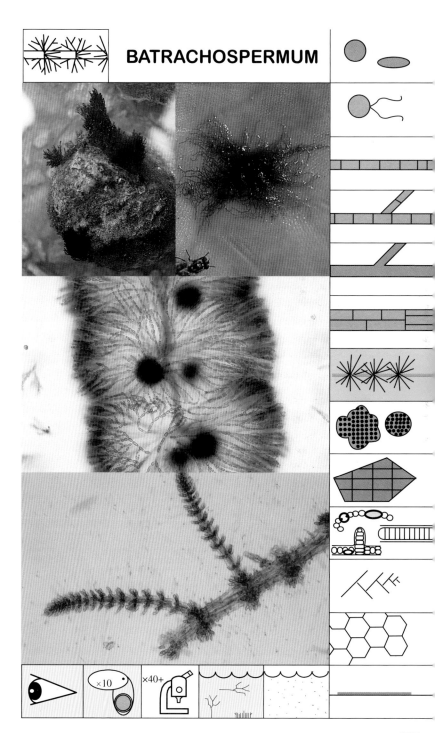

BATRACHOSPERMUM

135

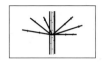

CHARA

Habitat: Attached in sand or soil, in fresh to somewhat brackish water.

Colour: Green.

Habit: The main axis is surrounded by regular whorls of filaments. The axial cells are 0.2–3.5 mm diameter and usually covered by closely adhering longitudinal filaments; stipulodes (single-celled structures at axial nodes) are inserted between each branchlet in one or two tiers, but some are sometimes rudimentary. The branchlets are undivided but with whorls of bract cells (single-celled structures at branchlet nodes).

Microscopic Features: The gametangia are borne at branchlet nodes or occasionally at base of whorl. The oogonium is directly below the antheridium, or isolated at a separate node or on a separate plant; it is crowned by a single tier of five cells.

Classification: Division Chlorophyta, Family Characeae.

Species and Distribution: 19 species, cosmopolitan; 16 species reported from Australia.

e.g.   *Chara corallina*: East Africa through Asia to New Zealand; WA, NT, SA, Qld, NSW, Vic., Tas.

Chara fibrosa: cosmopolitan; WA, NT, SA, Qld, NSW, Vic., Tas.

Chara vulgaris: cosmopolitan; WA, SA, Qld, NSW, ACT, Vic., Tas.

Notes: *Chara* is common in freshwater habitats with silty or sandy substrates. Variants of *C. corallina* with male and female gametangia on separate individuals are sometimes referred to as *C. australis.* Two similar genera also occur in Australia. *Lamprothamnium* is similar to 'uncorticated' species of *Chara* but the stipulodes are inserted beneath each branchlet (in a single tier) and are long and tapered. A single species, *L. papulosum*, is reported from all States except NT but is more widespread in southern Australia. The genus *Lynchnothamnus*, reported from a single locality in Qld, also resembles 'uncorticated' species of *Chara* (see publications listed at the end of this guide for distinguishing features).

Compare With: *Nitella.*

Caption:
Chara actual size (photograph), X 8 (left drawing, middle drawing).
Lamprothamnium, a similar charophyte, X 8 (right drawing).

CHARA

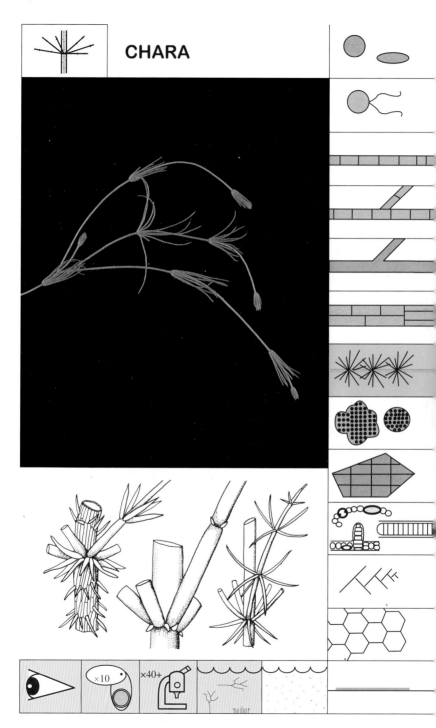

137

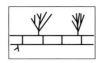

DRAPARNALDIA

Habitat: Attached to rocks in cool flowing water.

Colour: Bright green.

Habit: The bead-like thallus readily disintegrates after being removed from water. It consists of a main axis of broad cells with lateral branches of limited growth arising at irregular intervals.

Microscopic Features: The cells of the main axis are c. 20–60 μm diameter with cylindrical, sometimes fringed, chloroplasts and one to several pyrenoids. The lateral branches consist of narrower filaments, c. 5–15 μm diameter, usually determinate in length.

Classification: Division Chlorophyta, Family Chaetophoraceae.

Species and Distribution: 5–6 species, cosmopolitan; apparently one species from Australia.

Draparnaldia mutabilis: cosmopolitan; WA, Qld, NSW, Vic.

Notes: *Draparnaldia* is common in cool streams, particularly in spring, and sometimes forms extensive growths. *Draparnaldiopsis* is similar but the central axis consists of regularly alternating long and short cells with determinate laterals arising from only the short cells. It has been reported from northern NSW and Qld.

Compare With: *Batrachospermum, Chaetophora, Stigeoclonium.*

Caption:
Draparnaldia X 150 (top), X 100 (middle), main axis X 400 (bottom-left), tip of thallus X 60 (bottom-right).

DRAPARNALDIA

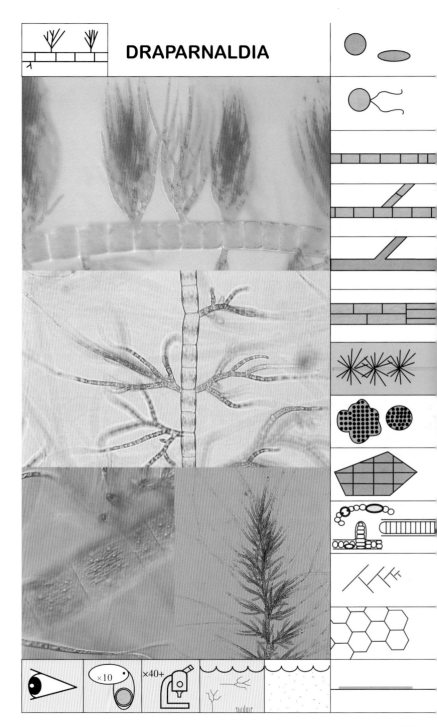

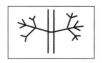

NITELLA

Habitat: Attached in sand or soil in still or flowing freshwater, occasionally in brackish water.

Colour: Green.

Habit: The main axis is surrounded by whorls of filaments. The axial cells are 0.2–1.0 mm diameter and not corticated with longitudinal filaments; stipulodes (single-celled structures at axial nodes) beneath branchlets are absent. The branchlets are divided one or more times into similar, 1–3 celled sub-branchlets, or with smaller 'fertile' whorls, usually without a central axis. Bract cells (single-celled structures at branchlet nodes) are absent.

Microscopic Features: The gametangia are together at the same node or at separate nodes or at separate plants. Oogonia are usually lateral at a branchlet node, compressed, and crowned by ten cells in two tiers. The antheridia are generally at the end of the branchlet or the base of a whorl.

Classification: Division Chlorophyta, Family Characeae.

Species and Distribution: 49–180 species, cosmopolitan; 24 species reported from Australia.

e.g.   *Nitella cristata*: Africa, south Asia; WA, SA, Qld, NSW, ACT, Vic., Tas.
       Nitella furcata: Madagascar through Asia to America; Qld, NSW, Vic., Tas.
       Nitella tasmanica: endemic: WA, SA, Qld, NSW, Vic., Tas.

Notes: *Nitella* is common in freshwater habitats with silty or sandy substrate, particularly in clean water. *Nitella furcata* includes variants sometimes referred to other species (e.g. *N. australiensis*). *Tolypella* is similar to *Nitella* but has a distinctive habit, with the reduced fertile branchlets forming bird's-nest-like 'heads' and the branchlets (arising from the main axis) 3–5 cells long, unbranched and unequal in length. Two species, *T. intricata* and *T. nidifica*, are reported occasionally from southern Australia (*T. nidifica* var. *glomerata*, however, is sometimes raised to species level).

Compare With: *Chara.*

Caption:
Nitella actual size (photograph, left drawing).
Tolypella, a similar charophyte, X 2 (right drawing).

NITELLA

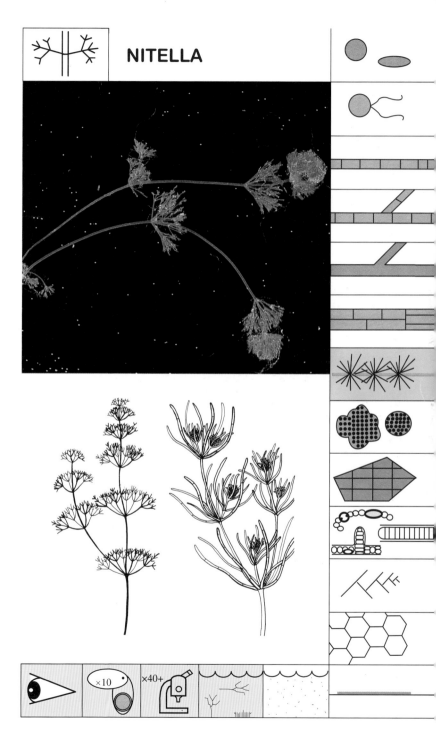

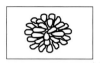

BOTRYOCOCCUS

Habitat: Free-floating in permanent and semipermanent pools and lakes, often near the surface of the water.

Colour: Green or yellow.

Habit: The irregularly globose colonies consist of groups of cells interconnected by strands of tough mucilage.

Microscopic Features: The ovoid cells are 5–12 μm long and more-or-less densely arranged in a single layer toward the periphery of the semi-opaque mucilaginous envelope. The cup-shaped chloroplasts form a network covering part of the cell wall and contain one pyrenoid.

Classification: Division Chlorophyta, Family Dictyosphaeriaceae.

Species and Distribution: Two or three species, cosmopolitan; two species reported from Australia.

e.g.   *Botryococcus braunii*: cosmopolitan; NT, Qld, NSW, Vic., Tas.

Notes: *Botryococcus* is widespread and may produce surface scums when in large numbers. If squeezed under a coverslip, *Botryococcus* exudes oily droplets that are similar in constitution to crude oil.

Compare With: *Dictyosphaerium, Pseudosphaerocystis.*

Caption:
Botryococcus with exuded oil droplets X 250 (top),
X 800 (bottom).

BOTRYOCOCCUS

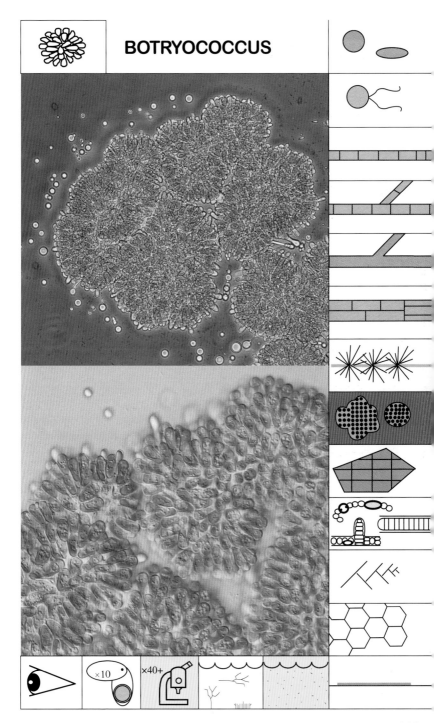

143

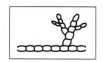

CHAETOPHORA

Habitat: Attached to rocks and aquatic plants; usually in alkaline water.

Colour: Green.

Habit: The globular or elongate gelatinous sacks are 2 mm to (reportedly from overseas) 15 cm across, and may be extremely tough in consistency. Branched filaments radiate from an attached base.

Microscopic Features: The cells are 5–15 μm diameter with a single sheet-like chloroplast and one to several pyrenoids. The ultimate branchlets often taper into a long multicellular hair or have a conical end-cell.

Classification: Division Chlorophyta, Family Chaetophoraceae.

Species and Distribution: About ten species, cosmopolitan; four species reported from Australia.

> *Chaetophora attenuata*: cosmopolitan; Qld.
> *Chaetophora elegans*: cosmopolitan; Vic.
> *Chaetophora punctiformis*: cosmopolitan; Qld.
> *Chaetophora tuberculosa*: New Zealand, Europe; Qld.

Notes: *Chaetophora* is reported occasionally, often from alkaline waters. It may be also confused macroscopically with *Coccomyxa* (not included here) which has been collected from soil in Tas. wet forest and heathland. *Coccomyxa*, which forms green jelly-like masses in damp shady areas, consists of small ellipsoid cells in a gelatinous matrix.

Compare With: *Nostoc, Rivularia.*

Caption:
Chaetophora X 10 (top), X 150 (middle), X 200 (bottom).

CHAETOPHORA

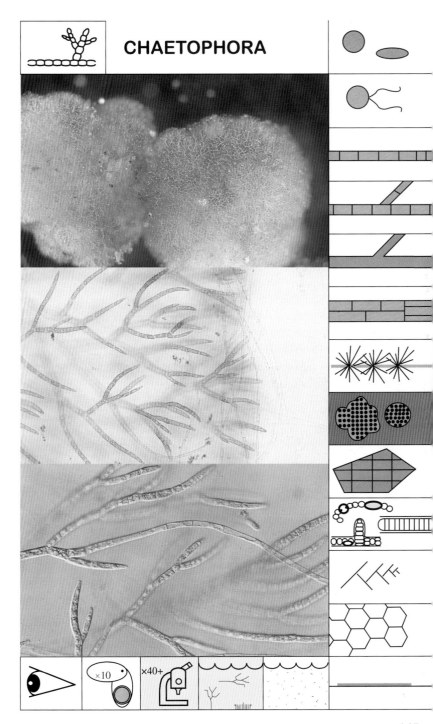

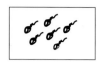

CHRYSONEPHELE

Habitat: Only in a swamp near Lake St Clair, Tas. The swamp is seasonally inundated with acidic (pH 4.6–6.8) water.

Colour: Pale golden.

Habit: A sack-like colony to 5 cm diameter, readily disintegrating when removed from water.

Microscopic Features: The mucilaginous cells are in a single peripheral layer and have two vigorously active flagella, although the colony is not motile. Each cell is 4–7 μm diameter and has one to several contractile vacuoles and a 2-lobed yellow chloroplast without a pyrenoid.

Classification: Division Chrysophyta, Family Ochromonadaceae.

Species and Distribution: One species, endemic to Australia.
  Chrysonephele palustris: Tas.

Notes: *Chrysonephele* is extremely localized. A yellow-brown colonial alga resembling the European *Celloniella* or *Chrysonebula* has been found in the Mt. Kosciusko area. It differs from *Chyrsonephele* in having immobile, differently shaped cells.

Compare With: *Chroomonas.*

Caption:
Chrysonephele X 0.6 (top), X 1000 (middle), X 1600 (bottom); the top and bottom pictures have been previously published in Tyler and Wickham (1988, figs 7 & 8).

CHRYSONEPHELE

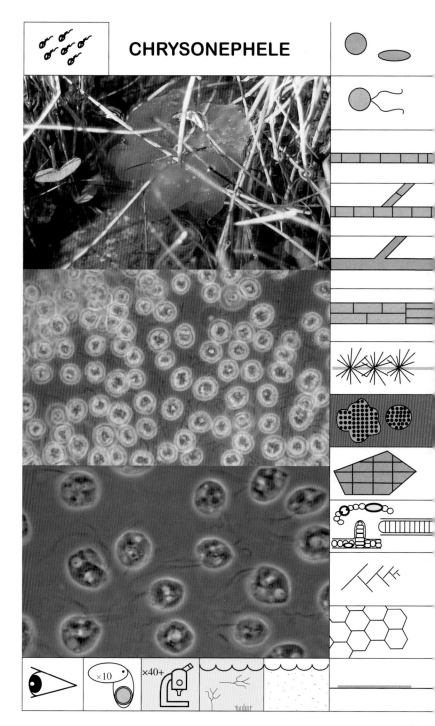

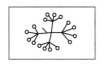

DICTYOSPHAERIUM

Habitat: Free-floating in lakes, ponds and semi-permanent pools.

Colour: Green.

Habit: The cells are connected by threads and contained within a fine gelatinous envelope (which is sometimes difficult to observe).

Microscopic Features: The spherical to ovoid cells are 4–10 μm diameter and borne terminally on a branched system of flattened threads (fibrils). Each cell contains one or two cup-shaped chloroplasts, each with a pyrenoid.

Classification: Division Chlorophyta, Family Dictyosphaeriaceae.

Species and Distribution: 12 species, cosmopolitan; three species reported from Australia.

e.g.   *Dictyosphaerium pulchellum*: cosmopolitan; NT, SA, Qld, NSW, Vic., Tas.

Notes: *Dictyosphaerium* is widespread.

Compare With: None in this guide.

Caption:
Dictyosphaerium X 600 (top photograph), colony in two focal planes X 1200 (middle-left, middle-right), X 1200 (drawing).

DICTYOSPHAERIUM

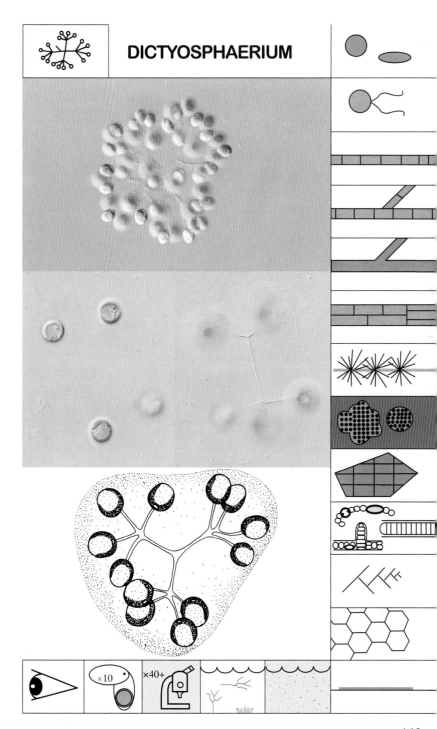

ELAKATOTHRIX

Habitat: Free-floating or attached in ponds and lakes.

Colour: Green.

Habit: The microscopic gelatinous, fusiform or irregularly shaped colonies contain a few elongate cells.

Microscopic Features: Each colony has two, four or more, fusiform or ovoid cells, 15–30 μm long and arranged in pairs within a common gelatinous sheath. The plate-like chloroplasts contain one or two pyrenoids, and cover almost all of the wall on one side. Asexual reproduction is by the formation of brownish akinetes.

Classification: Division Chlorophyta, Family Scenedesmaceae.

Species and Distribution: About seven species, cosmopolitan; two species reported from Australia.

Elakatothrix gelatinosa: cosmopolitan; NSW, Vic.

Elakatothrix viridis: cosmopolitan; Tas.

Notes: *Elakatothrix* is reported rarely but is apparently widespread. It was recently included in Klebsormidiaceae. *Quadrigula*, in the Oocystaceae, is a similar genus but the cells are parallel in compact bundles, rather than pairs.

Compare With: None in this guide.

Caption:
?Quadrigula, a genus often confused with *Elakatothrix*, X 400 (top, bottom), X 600 (middle). Unfortunately we were unable to photograph *Elakatothrix*.

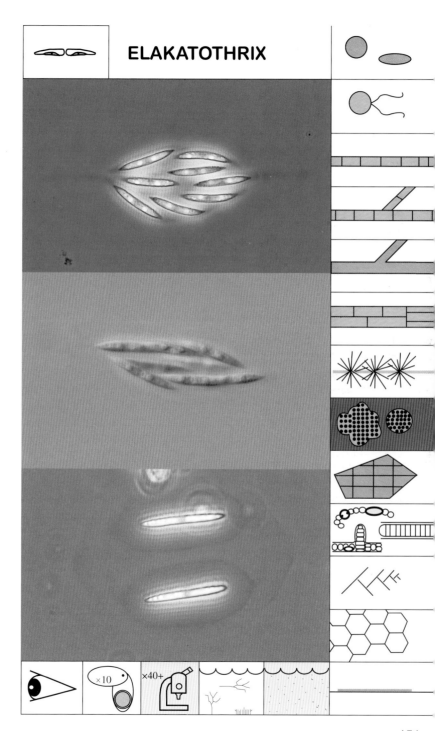

ELAKATOTHRIX

151

GONIUM

Habitat: Free-floating or free-swimming in pools and ditches.

Colour: Green.

Habit: The flat rectangular colonies contain 4, 16 or 32 cells.

Microscopic Features: The ovoid to pear-shaped cells are connected to one another by strong gelatinous strands, 5–15 μm in diameter. Each cell has two flagella and an eyespot. The chloroplast is cup-shaped and contains a single pyrenoid.

Classification: Division Chlorophyta, Family Volvocaceae.

Species and Distribution: 6–7 species, cosmopolitan; three species reported from Australia.

> *Gonium formosum*: cosmopolitan; NT.
> *Gonium pectorale*: cosmopolitan; Qld, NSW, Vic.
> *Gonium sociale*: cosmopolitan; Qld.

Notes: *Gonium* is widespread and common in most standing water. Colonies have a characteristic tumbling motion when actively motile. There are a number of very similar genera, differing in the shape and size of the colony.

Compare With: *Synura*, *Volvox*.

Caption:
Gonium X 1200 (top).
Eudorina, a similar genus, X 300 (bottom).

GONIUM

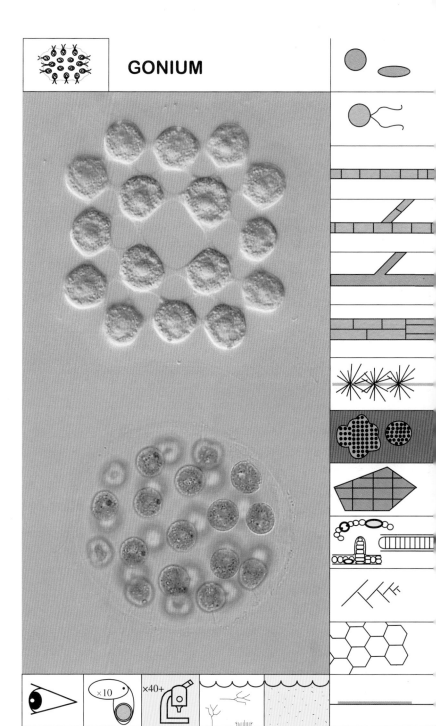

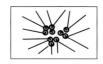

MICRACTINIUM

Habitat: Free-floating in large rivers and enriched wetland ponds.

Colour: Green.

Habit: The triangular colonies of 1–4 cells bearing long tapering spines are connected into a larger conglomerate.

Microscopic Features: The cells are 3–7 μm diameter and spherical to broadly ellipsoidal. Each group is, almost always, united with other groups to form a colony of up to 100 or more cells. Each cell contains a single cup-shaped chloroplast with one pyrenoid. There are one or two spines per cell and they may extend up to ten times the cell length.

Classification: Division Chlorophyta, Family Micractiniaceae.

Species and Distribution: Four species, cosmopolitan; one species reported from Australia.

Micractinium pusillum: cosmopolitan; NT, Qld, NSW, Vic.

Notes: *Micractinium* is common in enriched standing waters. It includes the genus *Errerella.*

Compare With: None in this guide.

Caption:
Micractinium X 1000 (top, middle-left); a pyramidal colony, sometimes referred to *Errerella* X 400 (middle-right), X 1200 (bottom).

MICRACTINIUM

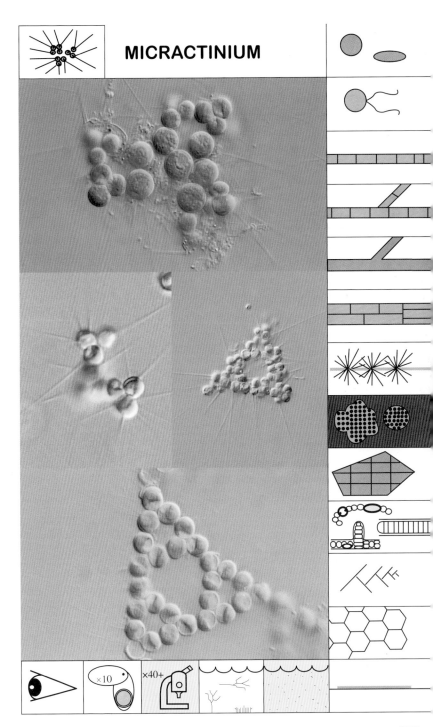

PALMELLOPSIS

Habitat: Attached to rocks in pristine to somewhat polluted streams, usually in cool water.

Colour: Green.

Habit: The cells are irregularly arranged in a cumulus-like gelatinous matrix.

Microscopic Features: The globose cells are c. 5–10 μm diameter, with contractile vacuoles and an indistinct cell wall. Vegetative cells lack flagella and pseudoflagella.

Classification: Division Chlorophyta, Family Palmellaceae.

Species and Distribution: Three species, cosmopolitan; one species reported from Australia.

> *Palmellopsis gelatinosa*: NSW, Vic.

Notes: *Palmellopsis* is found occasionally in south-eastern Australia. The identity of the Australian species needs to be confirmed (and compared with *P. texensis*). *Palmella*, a genus similar to *Palmellopsis* but without contractile vacuoles, is of dubious nomenclatural status: at least some species are referable to *Tetraspora* and many records probably represent stages in the life history of algae such as *Chlamydomonas*.

Compare With: *Tetraspora, Tetrasporidium, Tetrasporopsis.*

Caption:
Palmellopsis X 140 (top), X 350 (middle), X 1000 (bottom).

PALMELLOPSIS

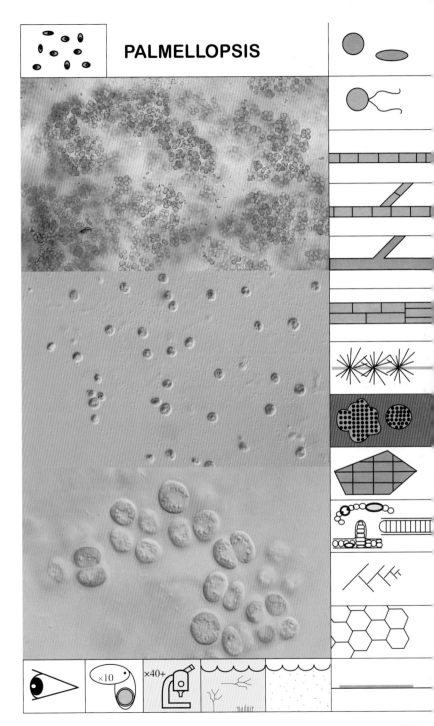

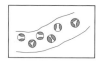

PALMODICTYON

Habitat: Attached to plants or other algae in sphagnum bogs, ponds and streams.

Colour: Green.

Habit: The gelatinous thallus is minute, simple, or branched and tubular.

Microscopic Features: The spherical cells are 4–20 μm diameter, and arranged irregularly or in a single row within the colony; groups of two or four cells may remain within a common matrix and the cast-off cell walls may persist. Each cell has several chloroplasts.

Classification: Division Chlorophyta, Family Hormotilaceae.

Species and Distribution: 3–4 species, cosmopolitan; three species reported from Australia.

e.g.   *Palmodictyon varium*: cosmopolitan; Qld.

Notes: In Australia, *Palmodictyon* is uncommon and apparently restricted to northern regions.

Compare With: *Chroodactylon.*

Caption:
Palmodictyon (all after Smith 1950, fig.58) X 250 (top-left), close-up of cells X 1800 (in circle), X 500 (right).

PALMODICTYON

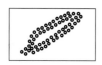

PARALLELA

Habitat: Attached to rocks or debris, or free-floating, in cool, acidic or neutral flowing waters.

Colour: Green.

Habit: The mucilaginous ribbon-like thallus is often much divided longitudinally.

Microscopic Features: Composed of parallel rows of paired cells, 5–11 μm diameter, without contractile vacuoles, flagella or pyrenoids; the chloroplasts are cup-shaped.

Classification: Division Chlorophyta, Family Palmellaceae.

Species and Distribution: One species, Australia, New Zealand, USA, Brazil.

> *Parallela novae-zelandiae*: Vic., Tas.

Notes: *Parallela* is widespread but uncommon in the streams of central and southern Vic. and northern Tas.

Compare With: None in this guide.

Caption:
Parallela X 80 (top), X 400 (middle), X 800 (bottom).

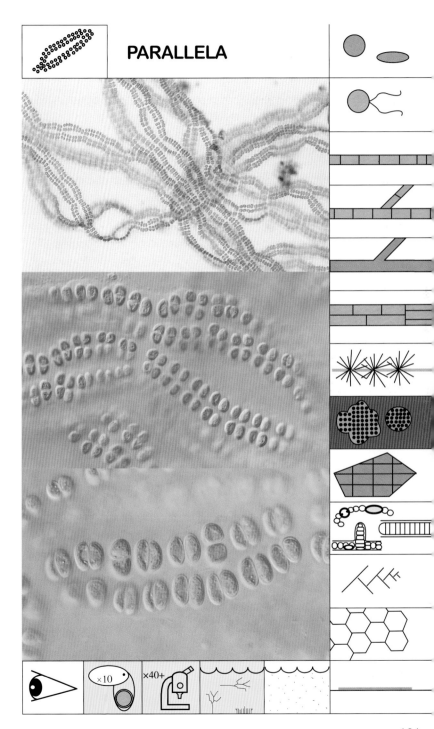

PARALLELA

PEDIASTRUM

Habitat: Free-floating in ponds, ditches and streams, often among plants or algae.

Colour: Green.

Habit: The cells are arranged in a flattened, stellate colony with 1–2-lobed peripheral cells.

Microscopic Features: The colony is contiguous or perforated (if there are more than 16 cells, the cells tend to be in concentric rings). The cells are 15–30 μm diameter, with a reticulate chloroplast and one pyrenoid.

Classification: Division Chlorophyta, Family Hydrodictyaceae.

Species and Distribution: 15–20 species, cosmopolitan; 14 species reported from Australia.

e.g.   *Pediastrum boryanum*: cosmopolitan; NT, Qld, NSW, Vic., Tas.
   Pediastrum duplex: cosmopolitan; WA, Qld, NSW, Vic., Tas.
   Pediastrum tetras: cosmopolitan; NT, Qld, NSW, Vic., Tas.

Notes: *Pediastrum* is widespread and common in most standing waters, and occasionally forms blooms. *Euastropsis* (not reported from Australia) is similar to *Pediastrum* but its colonies consist of only two cells.

Compare With: *Hydrodictyon.*

Caption:
Pediastrum X 500 (top), X 700 (middle), X 400 (bottom).

PEDIASTRUM

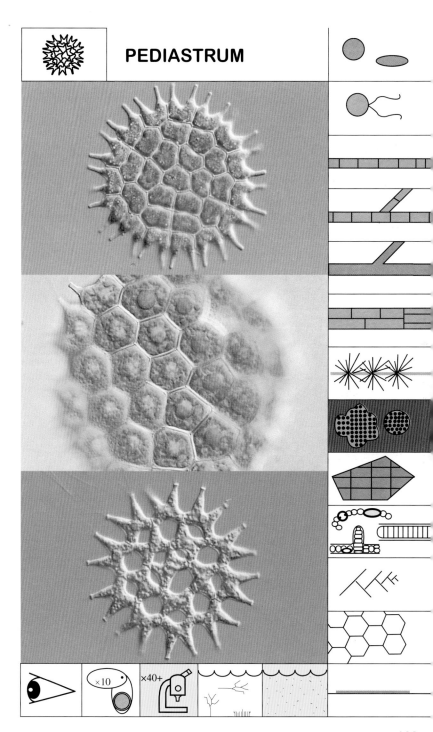

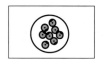 **PSEUDOSPHAEROCYSTIS**

Habitat: Free-floating in lakes.

Colour: Green.

Habit: The spherical colony contains 4–32 cells within a gelatinous envelope.

Microscopic Features: The spherical cells are 8–20 μm diameter and lie equidistant from one another near the periphery of a sometimes obscure gelatinous envelope. Each cell has a cup-shaped chloroplast with a single pyrenoid.

Classification: Division Chlorophyta, Family Palmellaceae.

Species and Distribution: Five species, cosmopolitan; one species reported from Australia.

> *Pseudosphaerocystis lacustris*: cosmopolitan; NT, Qld, NSW, Vic., Tas.

Notes: *Pseudosphaerocystis* is widespread. *Pseudosphaerocystis lacustris* has been previously known as *Sphaerocystis schroeteri*.

Compare With: *Palmellopsis, Tetraspora*.

Caption:
Pseudosphaerocystis X 250 (top), X 380 (middle), X 750 (bottom).

PSEUDOSPHAEROCYSTIS

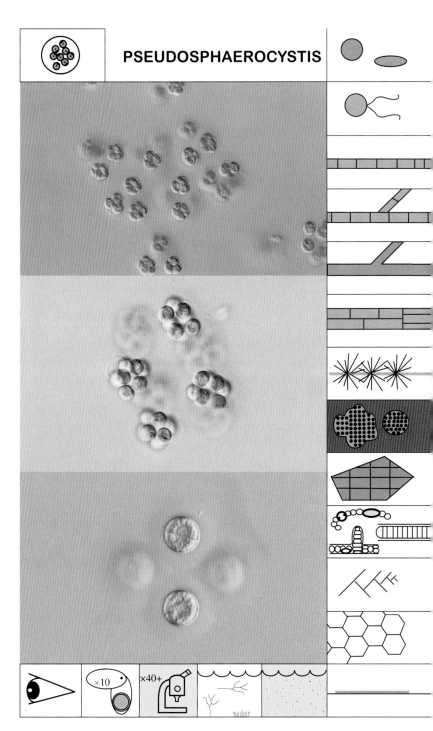

SCHIZOCHLAMYS

Habitat: Free-floating in lakes and ponds, or sometimes mixed with mosses or algae.

Colour: Green.

Habit: The irregularly-shaped colonies are minute or to 2 cm diameter.

Microscopic Features: The globose cells are 12–15 μm diameter, with groups of gelatinous pseudoflagella on one side. Chloroplasts are cup-shaped with a single pyrenoid. The old cell walls persist within the colonial matrix.

Classification: Division Chlorophyta, Family Tetrasporaceae.

Species and Distribution: 2–3 species, cosmopolitan; one species reported from Australia.

Schizochlamys gelatinosa: cosmopolitan; NT, Qld, Vic.

Notes: *Schizochlamys* is reported occasionally.

Compare With: None in this guide.

Caption:
Schizochlamys X 2000 (enlarged cell with flagella top right), X 800 (cells in matrix).

SCHIZOCHLAMYS

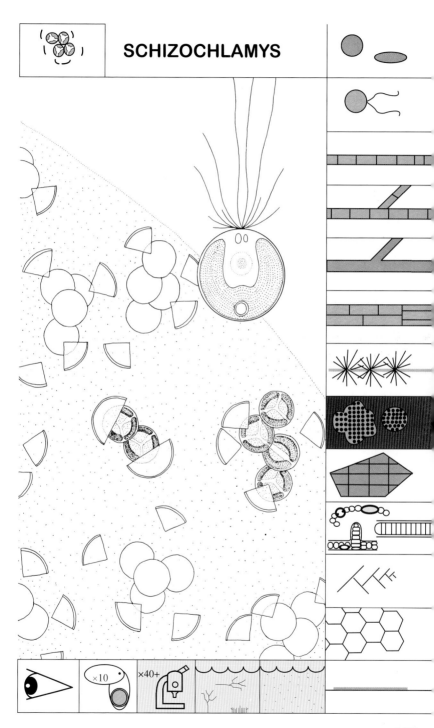

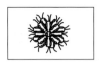

SYNURA

Habitat: Free-swimming in pools, ditches and lakes.

Colour: Yellow-brown.

Habit: The spherical to ellipsoidal colonies are free-swimming.

Microscopic Features: The pear-shaped cells are 30–45 μm long and stalked, radiating from a common centre. The cell membrane is covered with spirally arranged minute scales. Two curved chloroplasts lie along the walls of the cell with a large food granule at the base. There is no eyespot and the two flagella at the anterior of the cell are of the same length.

Classification: Division Chrysophyta, Family Synuraceae.

Species and Distribution: 12 species, cosmopolitan; ten species reported from Australia.

e.g.   *Synura petersenii*: cosmopolitan; NT, SA, NSW, Vic., Tas.

Notes: *Synura* is widespread and sometimes abundant. In large numbers it may produce a foul odour and taste.

Compare With: *Mallomonas.*

Caption:
Synura X 100 (top-left), X 500 (top-right), X 160 (middle-left), X 125 (middle-right), X 450 (bottom).

SYNURA

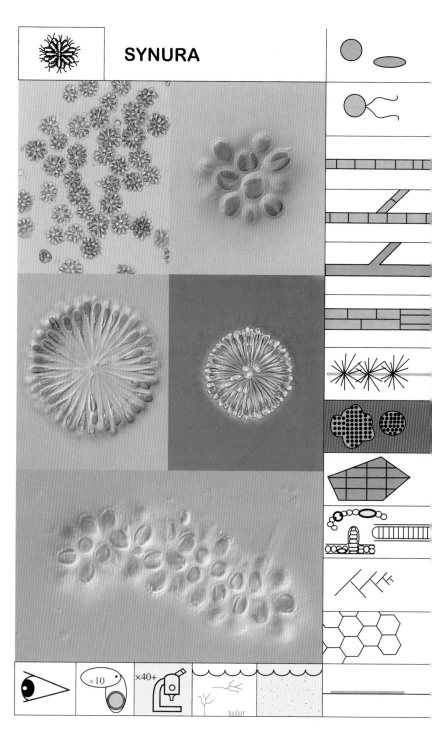

169

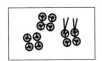

TETRASPORA

Habitat: Attached or free-floating in generally cold, flowing, or still water.

Colour: Green.

Habit: The sack-like, watery or tough matrix, is microscopic or up to 15 cm long.

Microscopic Features: The globose cells are mostly near the periphery of the sack, usually arranged in groups of four. they are more or less spherical, c. 5–10 μm diameter, and with a pair of pseudoflagella. The cell-wall is indistinct, the chloroplasts are cup-shaped with a single pyrenoid and 'contractile vacuoles' are present.

Classification: Division Chlorophyta, Family Tetrasporaceae.

Species and Distribution: 10–11 species, cosmopolitan; five species reported from Australia.

e.g.   *Tetraspora gelatinosa*: cosmopolitan; Qld, NSW, Vic.
        Tetraspora lubrica: cosmopolitan; NSW.

Notes: *Tetraspora* is reported occasionally, particularly in spring. The pseudoflagella (non-functional and modified flagella) can be difficult to observe, but the clusters of four cells are distinctive.

Compare With: *Palmellopsis, Tetrasporidium, Tetrasporopsis.*

Caption:
Tetraspora X 200 (top, middle-right), X 130 (middle-left), X 1500 (drawing).

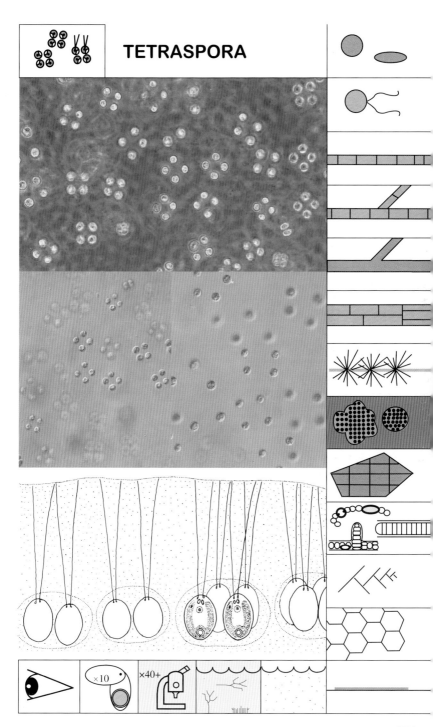

TETRASPORA

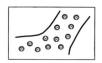

TETRASPORIDIUM

Habitat: Attached in shallow, often polluted, flowing water.

Colour: Green.

Habit: The mature thallus is a perforated sheet to c. 3 cm long or more.

Microscopic Features: There is a single outer layer of globose cells, 6–13 μm diameter, with cup-shaped chloroplasts, a pyrenoid and contractile vacuoles; pseudoflagella are absent and the cell wall is indistinct.

Classification: Division Chlorophyta, Family Gloeocystaceae.

Species and Distribution: 1–3 species, cosmopolitan; one species reported from Australia.

> *Tetrasporidium javanicum*: Europe to China; NSW.

Notes: *Tetrasporidium* is apparently rare in Australia. Some species of *Tetraspora* reportedly have a perforated thallus like *Tetrasporidium*, but cells in the latter genus are not grouped in twos or fours.

Compare With: *Palmellopsis, Tetraspora, Tetrasporopsis.*

Caption:
Tetrasporidium X 100 (drawing of colony), X 3000 (drawing of enlarged cell, left), X 125 (middle, bottom photographs).

TETRASPORIDIUM

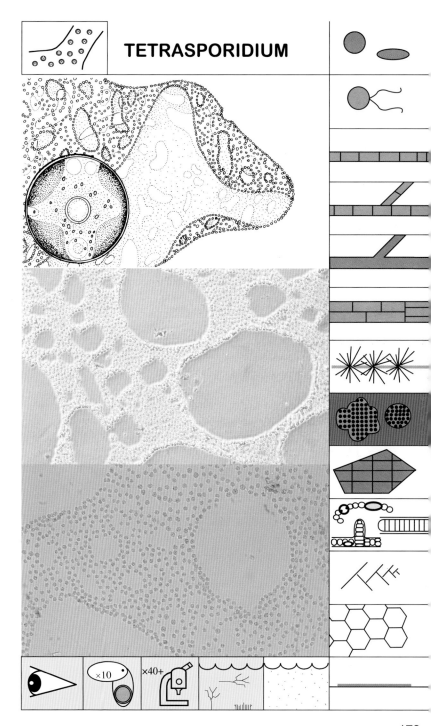

TETRASPOROPSIS

Habitat: Attached to rocks in slow- to fast-flowing streams in farmland or near-native forest.

Colour: Yellow-brown.

Habit: The sack-like colony (sometimes torn open) is up to 2 cm diameter.

Microscopic Features: The thallus consists of a single layer of randomly-spaced cells, each c. 10 μm diameter. There are 2–4 yellow-brown chloroplasts in each cell and contractile vacuoles are absent.

Classification: Division Chrysophyta, Family Chrysosphaeraceae.

Species and Distribution: At least one species, Europe, USA and Australia.

Tetrasporopsis fuscescens: Europe, USA; Vic.

Notes: *Tetrasporopsis* is of scattered occurrence but is possibly more widespread than meagre records suggest.

Compare With: *Palmellopsis, Tetraspora, Tetrasporidium.*

Caption:
Tetrasporopsis X 2.5 (top), X 500 (middle-left), X 200 (middle-right), X 3500 (drawing; both after Entwisle and Andersen 1990, fig. 2).

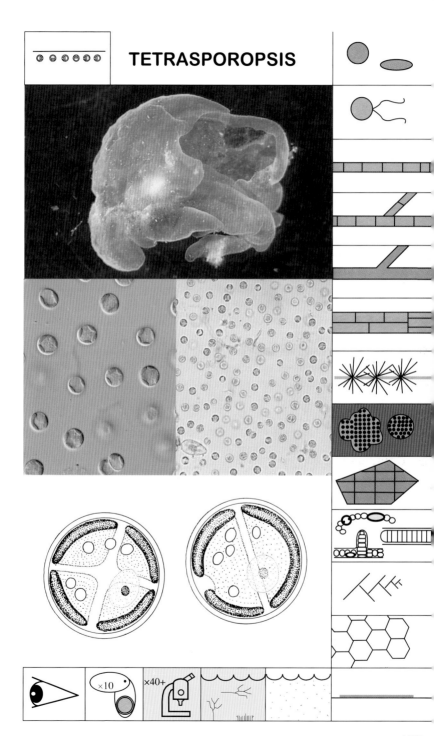

TETRASPOROPSIS

VOLVOX

Habitat: Free-swimming in ditches, lakes, ponds or other bodies of still water.

Colour: Green.

Habit: The spherical to ovoid colony is 0.5–1.5 mm diameter and usually visible to the naked eye.

Microscopic Features: The colony has a single layer of approximately 500 to 50,000 biflagellate *Chlamydomonas*-like cells surrounded by a mucilaginous envelope. Large colonies may contain one to several daughter colonies.

Classification: Division Chlorophyta, Family Volvocaceae.

Species and Distribution: c. 20 species, cosmopolitan; five species reported from Australia.

e.g.   *Volvox aureus*: cosmopolitan; NT, Qld, NSW, Vic.

    Volvox globator: cosmopolitan; Qld, NSW, Vic.

Notes: *Volvox* is widespread and common. It is a beautiful exhibit under dark background illumination.

Compare With: *Gonium.*

Caption:
Volvox X 60 (top), X 300 (bottom).

VOLVOX

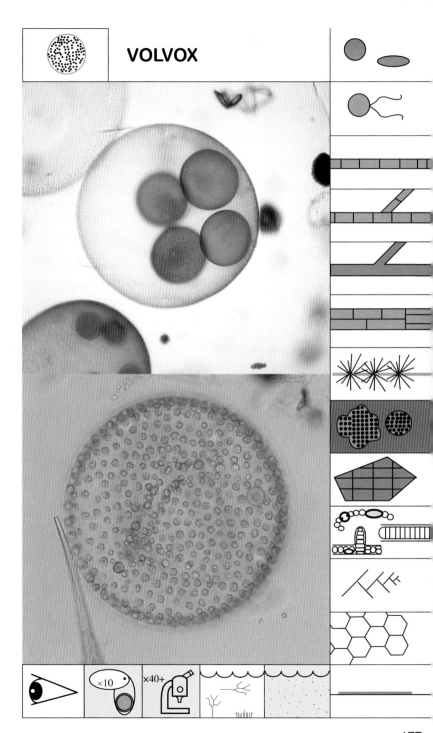

CALOGLOSSA

Habitat: Attached to roots or rocks, usually in coastal or near coastal streams.

Colour: Red-brown to olive-green.

Habit: The alga forms short tufts of leaf-like, lanceolate blades that are 2–5 mm long and 0.3–2 mm wide.

Microscopic Features: The thallus is anchored by colourless rhizoids produced at the constricted nodes between blades.

Classification: Division Rhodophyta, Family Delessariaceae.

Species and Distribution: About four species reported from freshwater, possibly all in Australian streams.

e.g. *Caloglossa leprieurii*: cosmopolitan; Vic.

Notes: *Caloglossa* is usually found in coastal or near-coastal streams, apparently favouring alkaline waters.

Compare With: None in this guide.

Caption:
Caloglossa X 4 (top), X 90 (middle), X 30 (bottom).

CALOGLOSSA

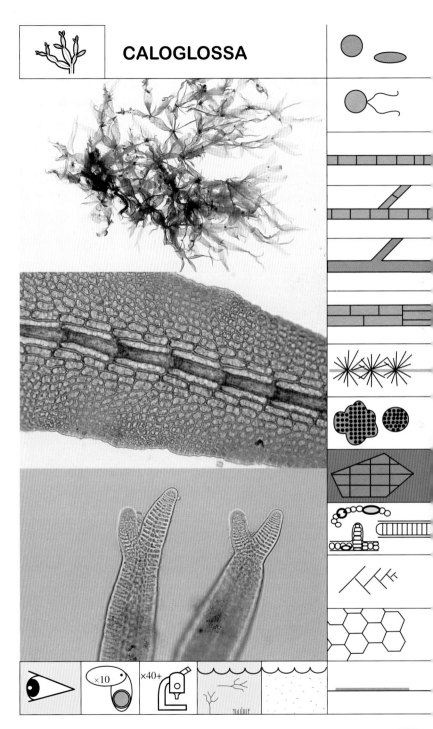

MONOSTROMA

Habitat: Attached or floating in fresh or brackish, still or flowing, water.

Colour: Green.

Habit: The young alga is sack-like, eventually splitting at the base into a broad sheet, one cell thick and up to 15 cm wide.

Microscopic Features: The compactly arranged angular cells are 5–50 μm diameter, and contain a single plate-like chloroplast.

Classification: Division Chlorophyta, Family Ulvaceae.

Species and Distribution: Doubtful number of species, cosmopolitan; five species reported from inland localities in Australia.

> *?Monostroma expansa*: endemic; Vic.
> *?Monostroma membranaceum*: cosmopolitan; Vic.
> *?Ulvaria oxyspermum*: cosmopolitan; Vic.

Notes: *Monostroma* is reported rarely from freshwater. The generic affinities of the sheet-like and tubular Ulvaceae from inland Australia need to be clarified. In addition to the difficulty in distinguishing *Enteromorpha* from *Monostroma*, there is also the distinction between *Monostroma*, without basal rhizoids and with an alternation of a large sheet-like thalli with a microscopic phase, and *Ulvaria*, with basal rhizoids and an alteration of similar-looking sheet-like generations, to be considered. This also effects the familial placement of the genera: *Enteromorpha* and *Ulvaria* are in the Ulvaceae, while *Monostroma* is now included in its own family, the Monostromataceae.

Compare With: *Enteromorpha*.

Caption:
Monostroma (or *Ulvaria*) floating in stream (top), folded portion of thallus X 60 (middle), cell arrangement X 200 (bottom).

MONOSTROMA

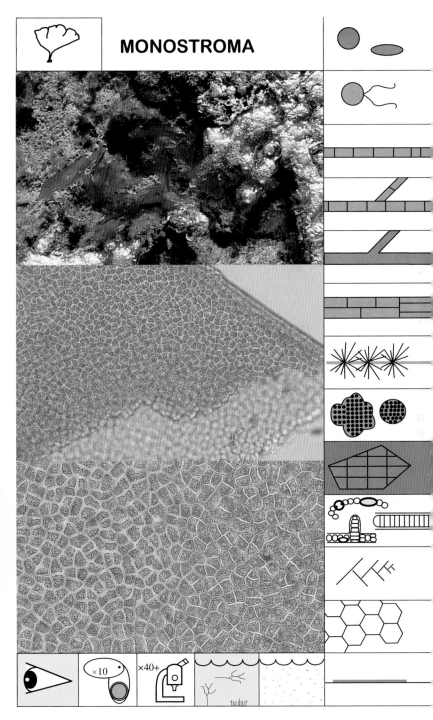

 **ANABAENA**

Habitat: Free-floating in slow-flowing or still waters.

Colour: Grey to blue-green or green.

Habit: The short unbranched filaments can be solitary or form a gelatinous mass.

Microscopic Features: The filaments lack a distinct sheath and are 7–12 μm diameter with the apices sometimes slightly attenuated. The cells are rounded, never discoid. The heterocysts (rarely absent) are also rounded or spherical, generally solitary and intercalary. Akinetes are single or in a long series, next to or distant from heterocysts and always larger than vegetative cells.

Classification: Division Cyanobacteria, Family Nostocaceae.

Species and Distribution: 60–70 species, cosmopolitan; 29 species reported from Australia.

e.g.   *Anabaena circinalis*: cosmopolitan; SA, Qld, NSW, Vic.

Anabaena flos-aquae: cosmopolitan; NT, SA, Qld, NSW, Vic.

Anabaena oscillarioides: cosmopolitan; NT, SA, Qld, NSW, Vic.

Anabaena spiroides: cosmopolitan; WA, SA, Qld, NSW, Vic.

Notes: *Anabaena* is widespread and seasonally abundant (throughout late spring to autumn). It is one of the toxic bloom-forming blue-green algae. Some species of *Anabaena* can produce a cocaine-like alkaloid called anatoxin-a which is a neuromuscular blocking agent causing respiratory arrest, liver and gastro-intestinal damage, and is possibly a carcinogen. Livestock may die soon after drinking water containing this toxin. Blooms of *Anabaena* can also cause contact irritations leading to severe dermatitis.

Compare With: *Microcystis, Nodularia, Nostoc.*

Caption:
Anabaena X 100 (top), X 450 (middle), X 700 (bottom).

ANABAENA

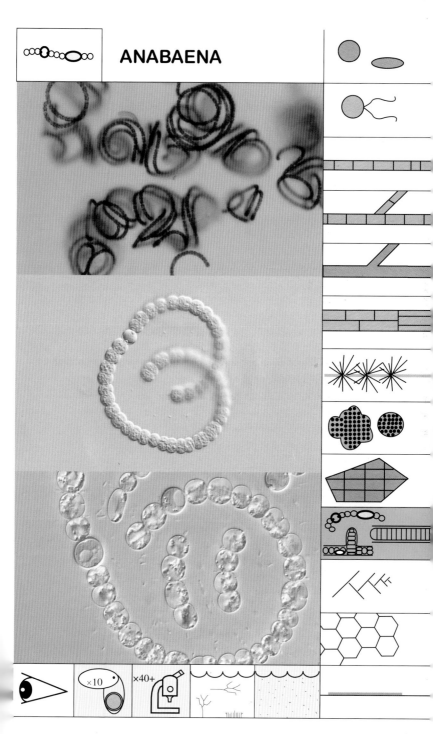

COLEODESMIUM

Habitat: Attached to rocks and debris in fast-flowing streams and large rivers.

Colour: Blue-greenish.

Habit: The coarse-textured tufts grow to 5 mm high.

Microscopic Features: The thallus is 25–85 μm diameter consisting of a thick sheath enclosing a number of filaments, usually without heterocysts. The anterior cell of the filament is hemispherical to almost spherical. Reproduction is by destruction and compression of intercalary cells causing the filaments to break into segments.

Classification: Division Cyanobacteria, Family Scytonemataceae.

Species and Distribution: 2–3 species, cosmopolitan; one species reported from Australia.

> *Coleodesmium wrangelii*: cosmopolitan; Vic.

Notes: *Coleodesmium* is apparently widespread in at least Vic. streams.

Compare With: *Audouinella, Scytonema.*

Caption:
Coleodesmium X 100 (top), X 300 (middle), X 500 (bottom).

COLEODESMIUM

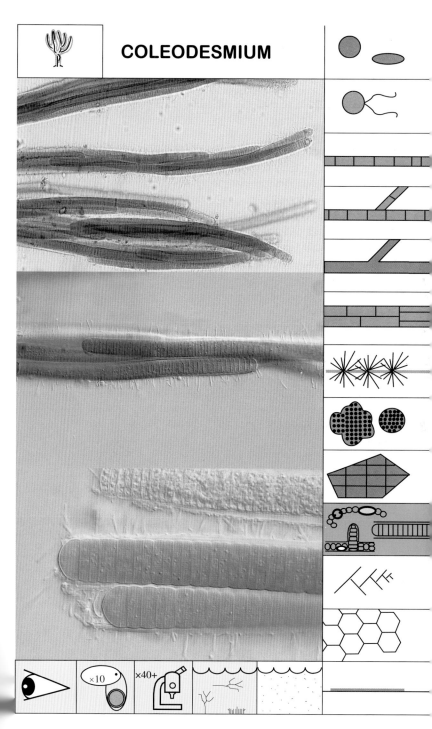

185

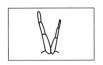

LOEFGRENIA

Habitat: Attached to rocks in streams.

Colour: Bright green.

Habit: The small tufts consist of erect filaments attached by mucilaginous pads and have no obvious gelatinous sheaths. Mature filaments gradually taper to a fine point.

Microscopic Features: The cells are 2–8 μm diameter and 3–15 times as long as broad. They are more or less cylindric and slightly constricted at the cross-walls. The anterior cells are sometimes colourless. Reproduction is by fragmentation into short cylindric to ellipsoid cells, 7–17 μm long.

Classification: Division Cyanobacteria, Family Loefgreniaceae.

Species and Distribution: One species, cosmopolitan.

    Loefgrenia anomala: NSW, Vic.

Notes: *Loefgrenia* is probably widespread in mountain streams of south-eastern Australia.

Compare With: None in this guide.

Caption:
Loefgrenia (not natural colour) attached to a stick (top), X 800 (middle), X 1000 (bottom).

LOEFGRENIA

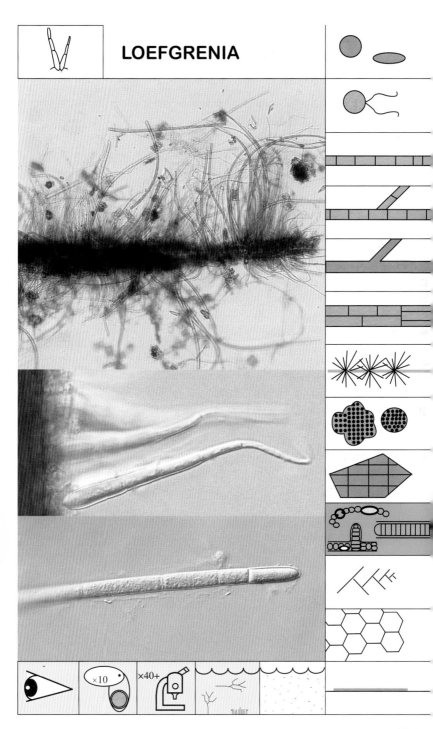

187

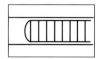

LYNGBYA

Habitat: Attached to rocks, sediment or other algae in ponds and streams, or on damp soil.

Colour: Blue-greenish.

Habit: Clumps contain filaments motile within a firm sheath.

Microscopic Features: The unbranched filaments are straight or slightly wavy, and mainly more than 6 μm diameter. The cells are shorter than broad or rarely as long as broad. Recently-divided cells rapidly divide again (before the previous division is complete or sibling cells have expanded to full size). The anterior cell usually has a thickened terminal wall or cap. Heterocysts and akinetes are absent.

Classification: Division Cyanobacteria, Family Oscillatoriaceae.

Species and Distribution: c. 65 species, cosmopolitan; 24 species reported from Australia.

e.g. *Lyngbya aerugineo-coerulea*: cosmopolitan; Qld, NSW, Vic.
Lyngbya major: cosmopolitan; NT, SA, Qld.

Notes: Some species of *Lyngbya* may cause contact irritations (possibly leading to severe dermatitis). *Porphyrosiphon*, a mostly terrestrial alga which can form coloured mats (e.g. red) in the dry country of inland Australia, differs from *Lyngbya* in having a lamellated sheath. *Lyngbya limnetica* is now referred to *Planktolyngbya subtilis*, not included in this guide.

Compare With: *Oscillatoria, Phormidium.*

Caption:
Lyngbya X 750 (top), X 2000 (middle).
Plectonema, a similar genus but with false-branching (branching not shown, but see *Scytonema*), X 2000 (bottom).

LYNGBYA

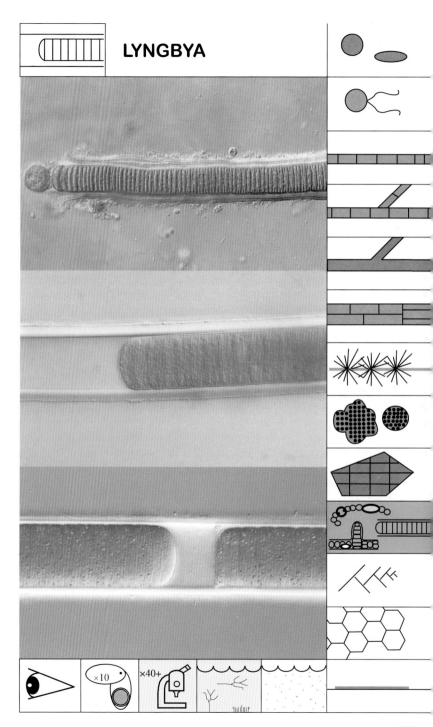

MICROCOLEUS

Habitat: Attached to submerged or damp soil.

Colour: Blue-greenish.

Habit: The filaments are bundled together in a single sheath.

Microscopic Features: The filaments are unbranched and 3–7 μm diameter; they are motile, and spiralled and tightly interwoven within the gelatinous sheath. The cells are shorter than broad. Heterocysts and akinetes are absent.

Classification: Division Cyanobacteria, Family Oscillatoriaceae.

Species and Distribution: 7–9 species, cosmopolitan; nine species reported from Australia.

e.g. *Microcoleus paludosus*: cosmopolitan; Qld.
      Microcoleus vaginatus: cosmopolitan; SA, Qld, Vic.

Notes: The circumscription of this genus varies between authors. *Microcoleus lyngbyaceous* is now referred to *Planktothrix planctonica*.

Compare With: *Lyngbya, Oscillatoria, Phormidium.*

Caption:
Microcoleus X 100 (top), X 600 (middle, bottom).

MICROCOLEUS

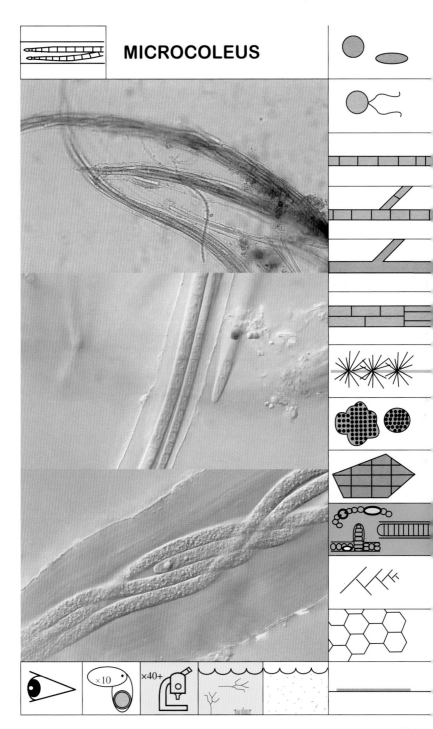

MICROCYSTIS

Habitat: Free-floating in lakes and reservoirs, sometimes in slow-flowing rivers.

Colour: Green, blue-green or yellowish-brown.

Habit: The colonies are globular to irregular.

Microscopic Features: The spherical or elongated cells are 0.5–5 μm diameter and usually densely arranged within a watery matrix. Cells may contain glistening or reddish gas vacuoles.

Classification: Division Cyanobacteria, Family Chroococcaceae.

Species and Distribution: 40 species, cosmopolitan; seven species reported from Australia.

e.g. *Microcystis aeruginosa* f. *aeruginosa*: cosmopolitan; WA, SA, NSW, ACT, Vic., Tas.

Microcystis aeruginosa f. *flos-aquae*: cosmopolitan; NT, NSW, Vic.

Microcystis wesenbergii: cosmopolitan; SA, Qld, NSW, Vic.

Notes: *Microcystis* is a common cause of algal blooms, sometimes secreting chemicals that inhibit other algae. It can produce a polypeptide called microcystin which is toxic to animals ingesting contaminated water and has been implicated in human illnesses such as necrosis of the liver (from ingestion) and severe dermatitis (from skin contact).

Compare With: *Anabaena, Nodularia, Palmellopsis.*

Caption:
Microcystis bloom in lake (top), X 200 (middle), X 400 (bottom).

MICROCYSTIS

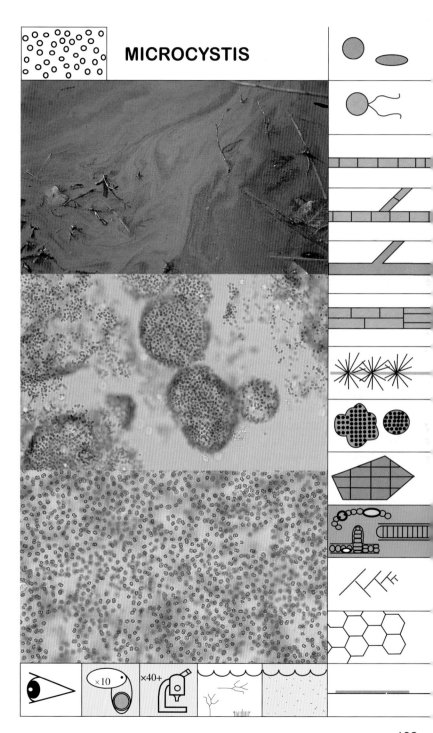

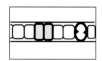 **NODULARIA**

Habitat: Free-floating in brackish, saline or freshwater lakes, intermingled with other algae or forming extensive blooms.

Colour: Blue-greenish.

Habit: The short unbranched filaments have a gelatinous but usually firm sheath.

Microscopic Features: The chain of cells is 4–18 μm diameter and not tapered. The vegetative cells, heterocysts and sometimes the akinetes are broader than they are long. The heterocysts are always intercalary, discoid, and generally a little broader than the vegetative cells. Akinetes are usually formed in a series of 2–12.

Classification: Division Cyanobacteria, Family Nostocaceae.

Species and Distribution: 12 species, cosmopolitan, one species reported from Australia.

Nodularia spumigena: cosmopolitan; WA, NT, SA, Qld, NSW, Vic.

Notes: *Nodularia* is widespread, sometimes forming extensive blooms which can result in the death of stock or native animals. It produces hepatoxins that can kill liver cells, leading to liver damage and gastroenteritis in humans.

Compare With: *Anabaena, Microcystis.*

Caption:
Nodularia bloom in lake (top), X 160 (middle), X 1000 (bottom).

NODULARIA

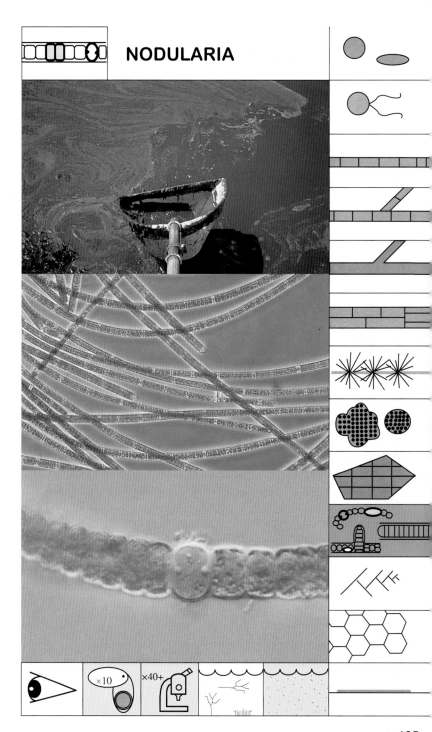

NOSTOC

Habitat: Attached to rocks or floating in streams and lakes; also forming dense colonies on damp soil.

Colour: Blue-green to brownish.

Habit: The chains of cells are irregularly arranged within a gelatinous or rubbery colony. These colonies are either small and planktonic, or up to 1–3 cm diameter (reportedly reaching 50 cm in some overseas specimens).

Microscopic Features: The filaments are 3–7 μm diameter, curved or contorted, and consist of globular cells. Heterocysts are intercalary, usually solitary, slightly larger, paler and with thicker walls than vegetative cells.

Classification: Division Cyanobacteria, Family Nostocaceae.

Species and Distribution: c. 50 species, cosmopolitan; 15 species reported from Australia.

e.g.   *Nostoc commune*: cosmopolitan; SA, Qld, NSW, Vic.

Nostoc linckia: cosmopolitan; Qld. Vic.

Nostoc sphaericum: cosmopolitan; Qld. Vic.

Notes: *Nostoc* is common and widespread. It is also part of some lichenized fungi and can grow within the thalli of certain bryophytes. *Nostochopsis* forms similar rubbery colonies but the filaments are long and branched.

Compare With: *Chaetophora, Rivularia.*

Caption:
Nostoc on rock removed from stream (top), X 3.5. (middle-left), X 140 (middle-right), 1000 (bottom-left).
Nostochopsis, a blue-green alga with similar habit, X 400 (bottom-right).

NOSTOC

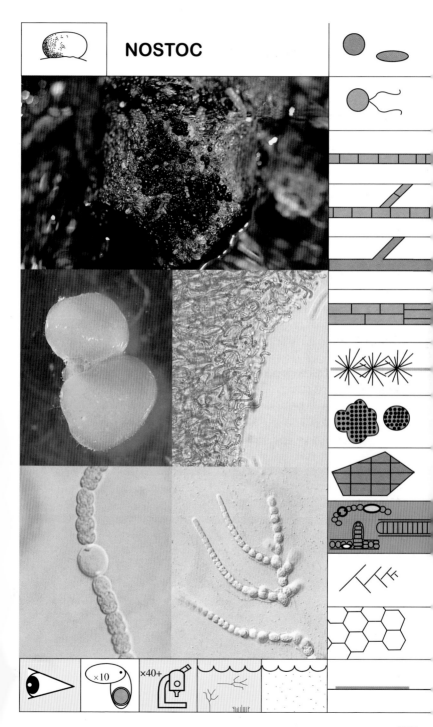

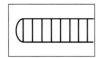 **OSCILLATORIA**

Habitat: Usually aquatic, free-floating or entwined with attached filamentous algae.

Colour: Blue-greenish.

Habit: The filaments are motile and able to glide to the top of muddy silt. A sheath is usually absent, but may be produced under suboptimal conditions.

Microscopic Features: The unbranched filaments are straight or slightly wavy and usually more than 8 μm diameter. The cylindric or discoid cells are shorter than broad. Recently-divided cells rapidly divide again (before the previous division is complete or sibling cells have expanded to full size). The anterior cell usually has a thickened terminal wall or cap. Heterocysts and akinetes are absent.

Classification: Division Cyanobacteria, Family Oscillatoriaceae.

Species and Distribution: 150 species, cosmopolitan; 47 species reported from Australia.

e.g.   *Oscillatoria limosa*: cosmopolitan; SA, Qld, NSW, Vic.
Oscillatoria princeps: cosmopolitan; NT, SA, Qld, NSW, Vic.
Oscillatoria tenuis: cosmopolitan; SA, Qld, NSW, Vic.

Notes: *Oscillatoria* is widespread and common in a variety of habitats. Some species may cause contact irritations (possibly leading to severe dermatitis). *Oscillatoria limnetica* is now *Pseudanabaena limnetica.*

Compare With: *Lyngbya, Phormidium.*

Caption:
Oscillatoria X 100 (top), X 850 (upper-middle), X 750 (lower-middle); Oscillatoriaceae, sometimes referred to *Oscillatoria*, X 1000 (bottom).

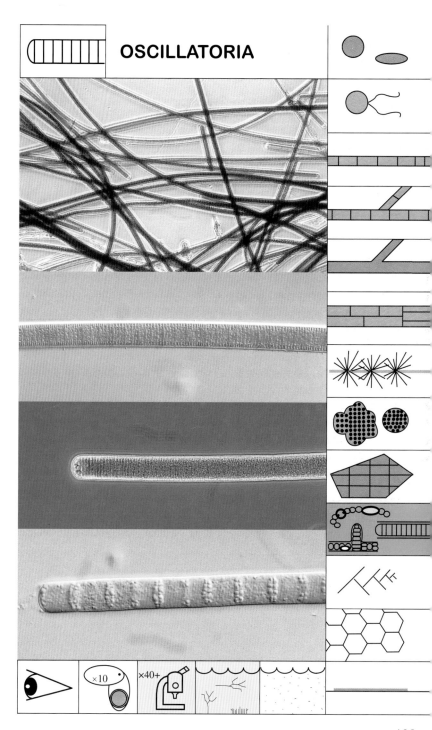

OSCILLATORIA

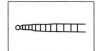

PHORMIDIUM

Habitat: Attached to rocks, debris or sediment in fresh and saline water; also on damp soil.

Colour: Blue-greenish.

Habit: The filaments form a coherent mass and rarely have false-branching.

Microscopic Features: The filaments are straight or irregularly undulating, and 1–12 μm wide. The delicate sheath contains a single motile filament. The barrel-shaped cells are shorter or longer than broad, and the end-cell is often tapering or conical. Recently-divided cells expand to full size before the next division. Heterocysts and akinetes are absent.

Classification: Division Cyanobacteria, Family Oscillatoriaceae.

Species and Distribution: c. 49 species, cosmopolitan; 20 species reported from Australia.

e.g. *Phormidium autumnale*: cosmopolitan; Qld, NSW, Vic.
Phormidium retzii: cosmopolitan; WA, Qld.
Phormidium tenue: cosmopolitan; Qld, NSW, Vic.

Notes: *Phormidium* is widespread and reported commonly.

Compare With: *Lyngbya, Oscillatoria.*

Caption:
Phormidium X 370 (top), X 1000 (upper-middle, lower-middle, bottom).

PHORMIDIUM

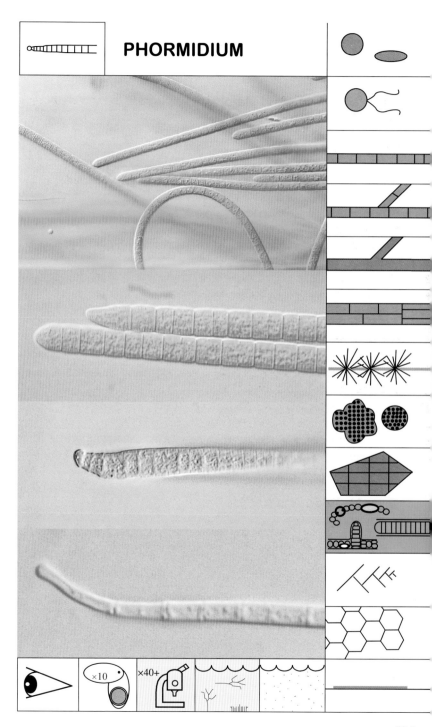

PSEUDANABAENA

Habitat: Usually tangled with other algae in streams and lakes; also terrestrial.

Colour: Blue-greenish.

Habit: Solitary, extremely narrow filaments.

Microscopic Features: The minute filaments are c. 1–2 μm diameter. The cylindric cells are separated or deeply constricted at the cross-walls, 3–4 μm long and longer than broad, and the anterior cell has a rounded end. Heterocysts and akinetes are usually absent.

Classification: Division Cyanobacteria, Family Oscillatoriaceae.

Species and Distribution: 12–13 species, cosmopolitan; five species reported from Australia.

e.g. *Pseudanabaena catenata*: India, Europe; NSW, Vic.
Pseudanabaena limnetica: cosmopolitan; SA.
Pseudanabaena mucicola: cosmopolitan; NT, SA.

Notes: *Pseudanabaena* is probably more widespread than meagre records suggest. *Limnothrix* is similar but has filaments not or only little constricted at cross-walls.

Compare With: None in this guide.

Caption:
Pseudanabaena X 250 (top), X 160 (middle), X 1000 (bottom).

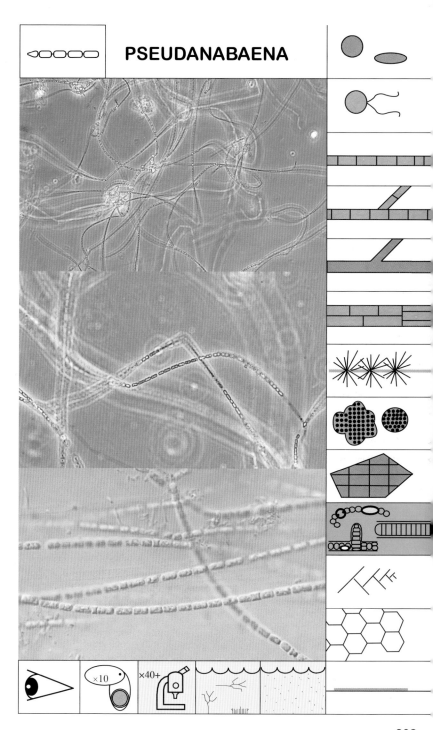

PSEUDANABAENA

RIVULARIA

Habitat: Attached to submerged rocks or plants; also on wet, exposed rock.

Colour: Blue-greenish.

Habit: The firm gelatinous colonies are up to 3 cm diameter and contain radiating, usually unbranched filaments.

Microscopic Features: The filaments are 4–13 μm diameter, tapering towards the tip, and have basal heterocysts. No akinetes are formed.

Classification: Division Cyanobacteria, Family Rivulariaceae.

Species and Distribution: 15 species, cosmopolitan; three species reported from Australia.

e.g.   *Rivularia beccariana*: cosmopolitan; Qld, NSW.

Notes: *Rivularia* is reported occasionally from freshwater, particularly in the streams of NSW and Qld. *Gloeotrichia* is similar but has an elongate akinete adjacent to the heterocyst.

Compare With: *Chaetophora, Nostoc.*

Caption:
Rivularia colony attached to *Myriophyllum* X 2 (top-left), X 20 (top-right), X 80 (middle-left), X 150 (middle-right), X 700 (upper drawing).
Gloeotrichia, a similar genus, X 700 (lower drawing).

RIVULARIA

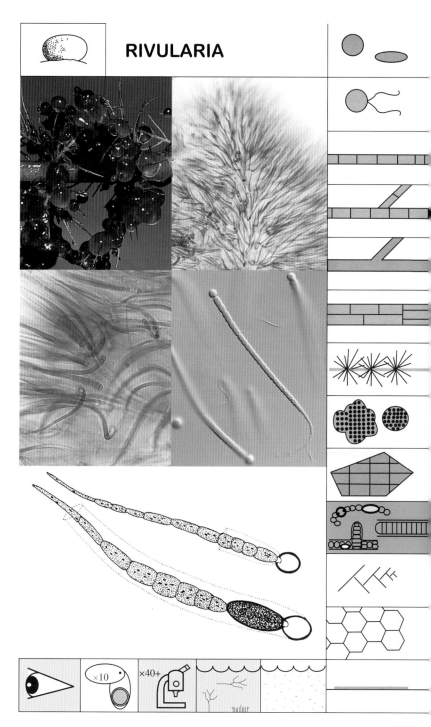

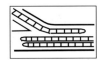

SCHIZOTHRIX

Habitat: Free-floating or attached in streams and lakes; also on damp soil and dripping rocks.

Colour: Blue-greenish.

Habit: The shiny, mucilaginous masses contain bundles of filaments with false-branching.

Microscopic Features: The filaments are 1–13 μm diameter, straight or slightly wavy, and not motile within the firm wide sheath. The sheaths are usually lamellated and include several to many filaments. Cells are usually longer than broad. Heterocysts and akinetes are absent.

Classification: Division Cyanobacteria, Family Oscillatoriaceae.

Species and Distribution: c. 26 species, cosmopolitan; eight species reported from Australia.

e.g.   *Schizothrix arenaria*: cosmopolitan; Qld, Vic.
        Schizothrix calcicola: cosmopolitan; SA, Qld, NSW.
        Schizothrix friesii: cosmopolitan; Qld, NSW, Vic.

Notes: *Schizothrix* is widespread but sometimes confused with *Oscillatoria* and other filamentous blue-green algae due to uncertain application of generic names. Some species form potentially noxious blooms.

Compare With: *Coleodesmium.*

Caption:
Schizothrix X 200 (top), stained X 500 (middle), stained X 1000 (bottom).

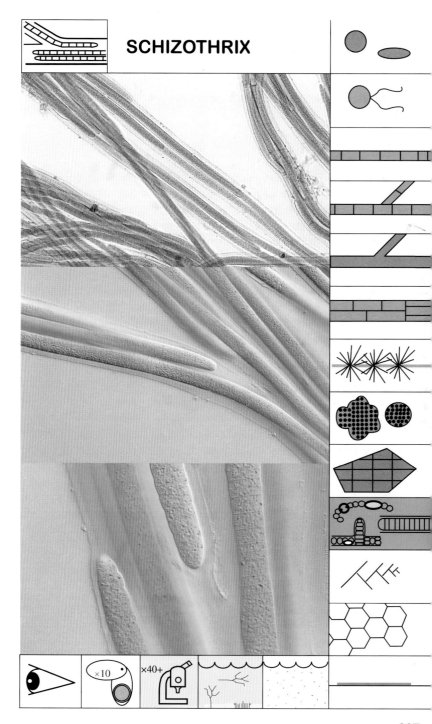

SCHIZOTHRIX

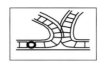

SCYTONEMA

Habitat: Attached to damp soil or wet rocky cliffs, or sometimes aquatic.

Colour: Blue-greenish.

Habit: The felt-like masses consist of filaments with false branching and a generally firm sheath. Pairs of filaments emerge midway between two heterocysts.

Microscopic Features: The cells are discoid or cylindric, 6–30 μm diameter, and are usually constricted at the cross walls. Heterocysts are single or 2–3 in a chain. A narrow, homogenous or lamellated sheath encloses a single filament. Akinetes are rare.

Classification: Division Cyanobacteria, Family Scytonemataceae.

Species and Distribution: c. 40 species, cosmopolitan; nine species reported from Australia.

e.g.   *Scytonema hofmannii*: cosmopolitan; Qld, NSW, Vic.

Notes: *Scytonema* is reported occasionally. As with many blue-green algae, it is a nebulous genus and species concepts make accurate identification difficult. *Plectonema* is similar but has filaments arising singly or in pairs at false-branches, and does not have heterocysts.

Compare With: *Coleodesmium* (some literature records of *S. hofmannii* are misidentified *Coleodesmium*), *Tolypothrix.*

Caption:
Scytonema X 75 (top), X 1500 (middle), X 1000 (bottom).

SCYTONEMA

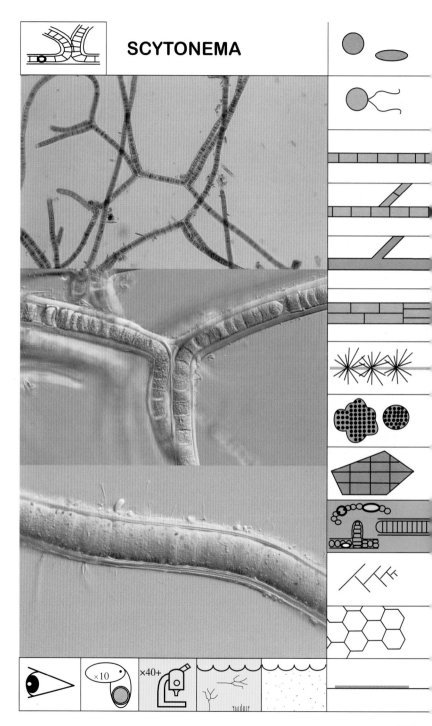

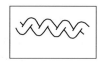

SPIRULINA

Habitat: Attached or tangled with other algae in stagnant water, ponds and lakes.

Colour: Blue-greenish.

Habit: The filaments are coiled, and solitary or in thin mats.

Microscopic Features: The filaments are 1–5 μm diameter, always regularly coiled (like a screw) and motile within the sheath. The cell walls are lined with granules.

Classification: Division Cyanobacteria, Family Oscillatoriaceae.

Species and Distribution: 7–9 species, cosmopolitan; nine species reported from Australia.

e.g. *Spirulina laxissima*: cosmopolitan; SA, NSW.

Spirulina major: cosmopolitan; SA, Qld, NSW.

Spirulina princeps: cosmopolitan; NT, Qld.

Spirulina subsalsa: cosmopolitan; Qld, NSW.

Notes: *Spirulina* is probably widespread. The circumscription of this genus varies between authors. The genus *Arthrospira* is sometimes split from *Spirulina*: it has broad filaments that are less tightly coiled.

Compare With: None in this guide.

Caption:
Spirulina X 100 (top), X 500 (middle-left), X 300 (middle-right).
Arthrospira, a genus sometimes separated from *Spirulina*, X 700 (bottom).

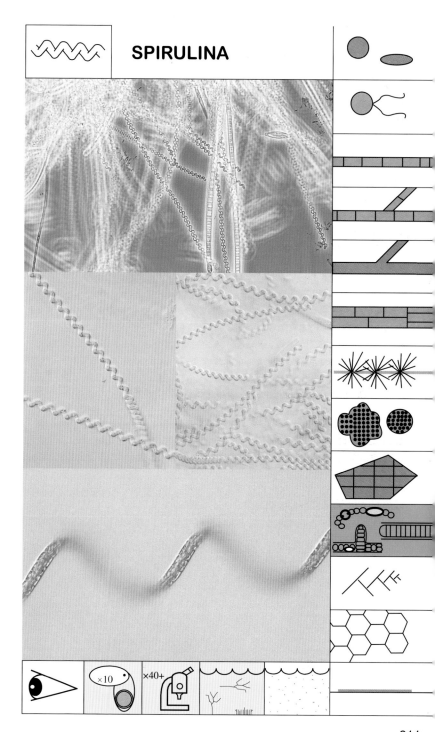

SPIRULINA

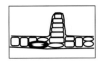

STIGONEMA

Habitat: Attached to rocks in pristine mountain streams; also on wet rocks or damp soil.

Colour: Brown to blackish.

Habit: The brittle thallus is irregularly branched and at least partly more than one cell thick.

Microscopic Features: The thallus is 25–70 μm diameter. The cells are discoid to globular, and heterocysts are present. The sheath is firm with a homogenous or lamellated surface.

Classification: Division Cyanobacteria, Family Stigonemataceae.

Species and Distribution: c. 30 species, cosmopolitan; seven species reported from Australia.

e.g. *Stigonema hormoides*: cosmopolitan; Qld.

Stigonema mamillosum: cosmopolitan; Qld, NSW, Vic.

Stigonema ocellatum: cosmopolitan; Qld.

Notes: *Stigonema* is abundant in some higher altitude streams at about water-surface level, but can grow fully submerged. *Hapalosiphon* differs from *Stigonema* in being one cell thick throughout.

Compare With: *Batrachospermum, Bostrychia*.

Caption:
Stigonema on emergent rock in stream (top-left), X 150 (top-right), X 800 (middle-left), X 400 (middle-right), X 300 (lower drawing). *Hapalosiphon*, a similar genus, X 800 (upper drawing).

STIGONEMA

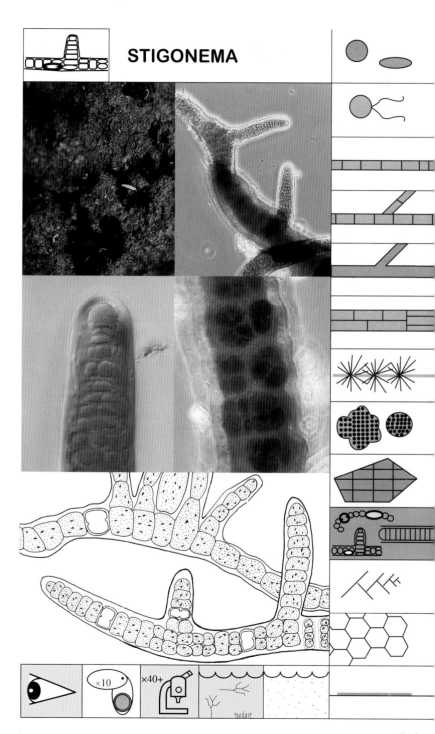

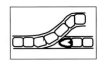

TOLYPOTHRIX

Habitat: Attached to rocks, plants, debris or sediment in lakes and streams; also on damp soil.

Colour: Blue-greenish.

Habit: The filaments have false-branching and a generally firm sheath. A single filament emerges immediately adjacent to a heterocyst.

Microscopic Features: A narrow, homogenous or lamellated sheath encloses a single filament. The cells are discoid or cylindrical, 5–12 μm diameter, and usually constricted at the cross walls. Heterocysts are single or in a chain of 2–6.

Classification: Division Cyanobacteria, Family Nostocaceae.

Species and Distribution: c. 18 species, cosmopolitan; six species reported from Australia.

e.g.   *Tolypothrix tenuis*: cosmopolitan; Qld.

Notes: *Tolypothrix* is reported rarely. It is able to form large mats on sediment at the edge of streams.

Compare With: *Scytonema.*

Caption:
Tolypothrix X 250 (top), X 1500 (middle), X 1000 (bottom).

TOLYPOTHRIX

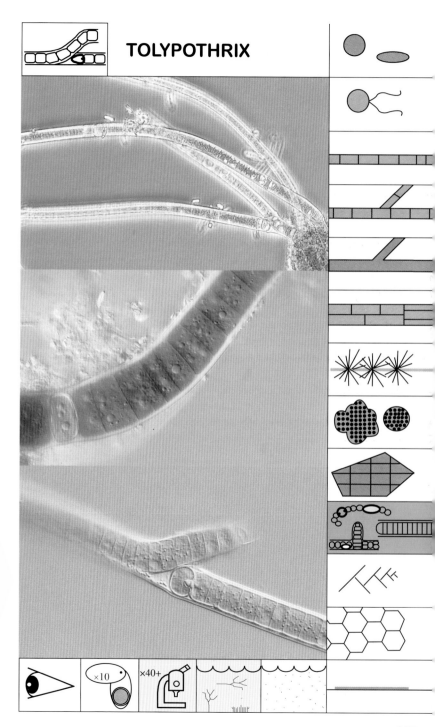

PTILOTHAMNION

Habitat: On rocks in a pool below a heavily shaded waterfall.

Colour: Dark purple-brown.

Habit: The cushion-shaped colonies are up to 7 mm diameter and 1 mm thick.

Microscopic Features: This alga consists of a prostrate system of irregularly branched filaments, giving rise to numerous erect filaments with a zigzag axis and regular pinnate branches in one plane. The cells are 10–25 μm diameter.

Classification: Division Rhodophyta, Family Ceramiaceae.

Species and Distribution: Two species, one in North and South America, the other endemic to Australia.

Ptilothamnion umbracolens: Qld.

Notes: *Ptilothamnion* is extremely rare and was not found in the one published locality (near Qld-NSW border) on two recent visits. It was previously called *Anfractutofilum.* Other intriguing algae perhaps allied to this genus are also known from inland waters in Qld.

Compare With: *Chroodactylon, Audouinella.*

Caption:
Ptilothamnion (both after Cribb 1965, fig. 1) cross-section through cushion X 30 (top), X 300 (bottom).

PTILOTHAMNION

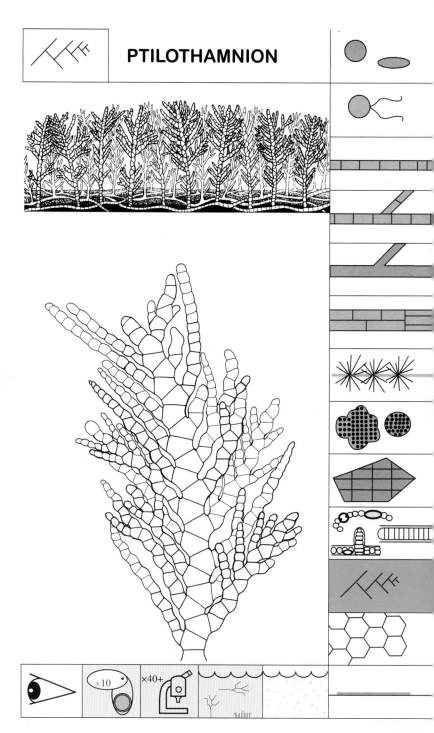

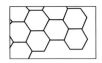

HYDRODICTYON

Habitat: Free-floating in lakes, slow-flowing streams and ditches.

Colour: Green or yellow-green.

Habit: The thallus is a large perforated sack or flat sheet.

Microscopic Features: The elongate cells are up to 8 mm long and 200 μm broad and arranged in a net-like pattern; chloroplasts are irregularly ribbon-like at first but become net-like, with a pyrenoid at most intersections.

Classification: Division Chlorophyta, Family Hydrodictyaceae.

Species and Distribution: Six species, cosmopolitan; one species reported from Australia.

Hydrodictyon reticulatum: cosmopolitan; Qld, NSW, ACT, Vic.

Notes: *Hydrodictyon reticulatum* can become a nuisance weed, choking small creeks and drains and appears to be resistant to herbicides such as copper sulphate. In Australia, *Hydrodictyon* appears to be less common in southern regions.

Compare With: None in this guide.

Caption:
Hydrodictyon X 0.3.

HYDRODICTYON

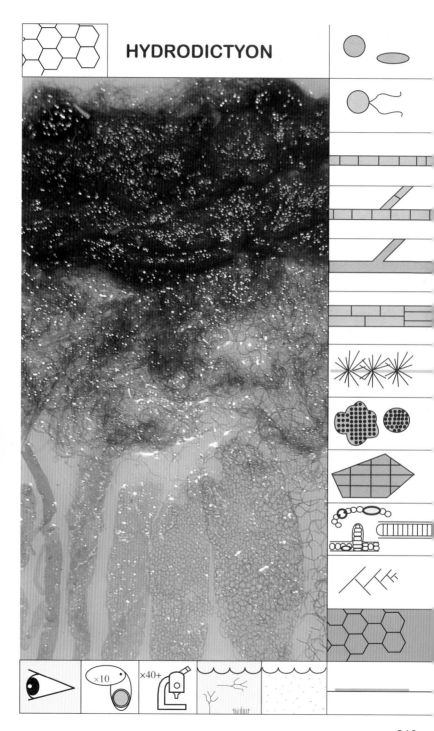

HILDENBRANDIA

Habitat: Attached to rocks in lakes or relatively fast-flowing streams.

Colour: Deep red to red-brown.

Habit: A crust (much like a paint stain) to 150 μm thick, 1–5 μm diameter.

Microscopic Features: The crust consists of tightly packed files of short, erect filaments. Cells are discoid to cylindrical and 4–6 μm diameter.

Classification: Division Rhodophyta, Family Hildenbrandiaceae.

Species and Distribution: 2 species, cosmopolitan; one species reported from Australia.

Hildenbrandia angolensis: North America, Africa; SA, Qld, NSW, Vic.

Notes: *Hildenbrandia* is reported rarely but is probably overlooked. Australian populations have been referred previously to the larger-celled Europe-Asia species, *H. rivularis*. Species differences are based primarily on cell size, and further collecting and observation is needed to determine which species are present in Australia.

Compare With: Aquatic lichens or some blue-green algal mats.

Caption:
Hildenbrandia on rocks in stream (photograph), X 2000 (upper-left of drawing), X 1000 (drawing).

HILDENBRANDIA

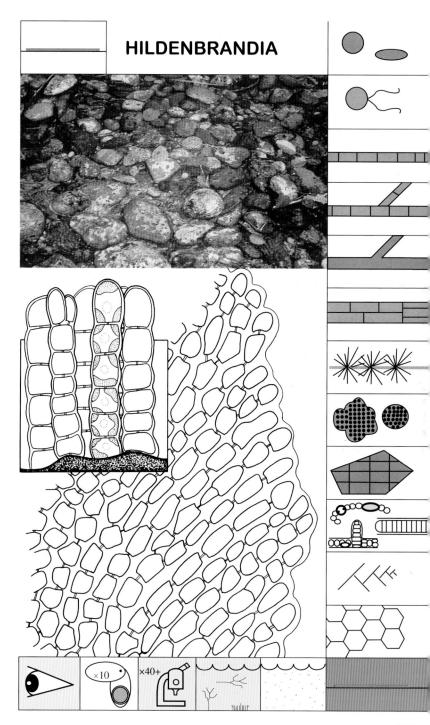

Glossary

μm Micrometre; 1 millimetre = 1000 micrometres.

Akinete A thick-walled, non-motile resting spore.

Alga (*pl.* algae) A commonly used term for photosynthetic organisms that are unicellular or with a unicellular sporangium.

Alginate An algal product used commercially as a thickening agent.

Anterior The forward end, toward the top.

Antheridium (*pl.* antheridia) The male sex organ; a spherical or elongated container which releases flagellate cells.

Aplanospore A potential zoospore that is never motile.

Axial Situated in the middle of a cell.

Axis The line about which structures are symmetrically arranged.

Biflagellate Possessing two flagella.

Bract cell A single-celled structure at branchlet nodes in Charophytes.

Branchlet A small branch.

Carotene An orange-yellow pigment, a hydrocarbon.

Cell The basic unit of an organism; in most algae consisting of various organelles inside a wall.

Chloroplast An organelle within a cell containing light-absorbing pigments; variously coloured but usually green or yellowish.

Cingulum Transverse furrow in dinoflagellates; e.g. *Peridinium*.

Colony A closely associated cluster of cells, joined together or enclosed within a common sheath or mucilage.

Conjugation Sexual reproduction between cells that connect together, with the entire cytoplasm from one cell fusing with that of the other and resulting in a zygospore.

Conjugation tube The connection between two cells involved in conjugation.

Cortex Outermost layer.

Corticate axis With an outer covering of longitudinally-arranged cells (giving a ridged or striped look).

Cosmopolitan Occurring throughout the world.

Cross-wall A wall that divides two cells, e.g. between cells in a filament.

Cytoplasm All parts of a cell outside the nucleus and inside the membrane.

Desmid A green alga belonging to the family Desmidiaceae; most are unicellular and divided into two equal portions, e.g. *Cosmarium, Micrasterias.*

Diatom A yellow-brown alga belonging to the division Bacillariophyta; most are unicellular and have a cell wall consisting of two overlapping silica shells, e.g. *Tabellaria, Cyclotella.*

Dichotomous Forking into two equal parts.

Ellipsoidal Water-melon shaped.

Endemic Having a natural distribution confined to a particular geographic region; *cf.* native.

Epiphytic Attached to a plant, but not parasitic.

Eutrophic Rich in nutrients.

Eyespot A red or brown cluster of granules that is sensitive to light.

False branching In Cyanobacteria, when the thallus, but not an individual filament, is branched; e.g. *Tolypothrix.*

Fibril Fine thread; e.g. in *Dictyosphaerium.*

Filament Cells in a linear series, usually abutting one another.

Flagellum (*pl.* flagella) Thread-like extension from cell used for locomotion.

Fusiform Broadest in the midregion and gradually tapering to both poles (three-dimensional).

Gametangium (*pl.* gametangia) Cells producing gametes.

Gamete A cell capable of uniting with a compatible cell as a part of the sexual process.

Gelatinous Jelly-like.

Globose Spherical or nearly so.

Gullet A cavity within a cell opening to the outside; e.g. *Cryptomonas.*

Hair A colourless, typically elongate, unicellular or multicellular structure.

Haptonema A microscopic appendage resembling a flagellum.

Heterocyst An enlarged cell in some filamentous blue-green algae, usually with thickened walls and highly refractive; presumed to be the site of nitrogen fixation.

Holdfast A cell, part of a cell or group of cells used for attachment.

Humic water Brown, tea-like water usually derived from peaty heathland.

Intercalary Intermediate in position, not terminal.

Isthmus The equatorial region connecting the semi-cells of desmids.

Lamellate With many layers.

Lanceolate Narrow, tapering at each end and broadest towards base.

Lorica A shell-like housing for a cell with an opening for the flagella; e.g. *Dinobryon*.

Macroscopic Visible to the unaided eye.

Matrix Watery or rubbery material containing algal cells.

Medullary Central region (inside the cortex).

Microscopic Hardly or not visible to the unaided eye; requiring magnification to see in the field.

Moniliform Arranged like a string of beads.

Motile Capable of motion.

Mucilaginous Slimy.

Multinucleate With many nuclei.

Native Naturally occurring in a geographical region, but not necessarily confined to it; *cf.* endemic.

Oligotrophic Low in nutrients.

Oogamous Sexual reproduction in which a small usually motile cell unites with a non-motile egg.

Oogonium (*pl.* oogonia) A female gametangium producing one or more eggs.

Ovate Egg-shaped in outline (two-dimensional).

Ovoid Egg-shaped (three-dimensional).

Paramylon body A solid, starch-like storage product or food reserve in the Euglenophyta.

Pit connection In red algae, a lens-shaped plug within the cross-walls between two adjacent cells.

Polypeptide A compound formed of many amino acids.

Pseudoflagellum (*pl.* pseudoflagella) Long, motionless flagella-like process, characteristic of Tetrasporaceae; often difficult to observe without phase contrast.

Pseudoraphe In diatoms, a longitudinal clear space separating two series of transverse markings.

Pyrenoid Usually a clearly delineated disc in the chloroplast; a protein body around which starch collects.

Receptor Part of an organism that receives stimuli from its environment.

Reticulate A network pattern.

Rhizoid Colourless filaments, often used for attachment.

Semi-cell One half of a desmid cell, often connected by a narrow isthmus.

Seta A stiff, bristle-like extension.

Sheath The covering around a colony of cells or an envelope around one or more filaments.

Sinus The invaginating region at the isthmus of semi-cells.

Siphon (*adj.* siphonous) A very long, tubular cell; a 'filament' without cross-walls.

Sporangium (*pl.* sporangia) Cell producing spores.

Starch Strorage product in many algae; used here to include a diverse range of insoluble polysaccharides.

Stellate Star-shaped; with radiating projections from a common centre.

Stipulode A single-celled process growing out from the base of the branchlet in Characeae.

Stratified In layers.

Striae A row of markings, or an elongate chamber in the siliceous wall of diatoms.

Symbiosis An association of two different organisms that is advantageous to both.

Taxon (*pl.* taxa) A member of any taxonomic category, e.g. genus, species.

Terrestrial Living on land rather than in water.

Thallus The overall form of a non-vascular plant.

Unicellular Consisting of one cell only.

Vacuole A fluid-filled space within the cytoplasm, bounded by a membrane.

Whorl Arranged in a circle around an axis.

Zoospore A flagellated, asexual reproductive cell.

Zygote The product of two gametes fusing, usually developing a thick wall.

Further Information

General References on Algae

Bold and Wynne (1985); Bourrelly (1968); Bourrelly (1985); Bourrelly (1988); Bourrelly (1990); Chapman and Chapman (1973); Christensen (1980–1994); Day *et al.* (1995); Entwisle (1994); Fritsch (1935); Fritsch (1945); Lee (1989); Prescott (1954); Prescott (1982); Smith (1950); Starmach (1968–1983); Sze (1986); West and Fritsch (1926)

Microscopic examination, staining and slide preparation

Johansson (1940); Berlyn and Miksche (1976).

Keys and descriptions for species

The general references cited above may also include useful keys to some species. Most of the references listed above and below deal with non-Australian species, so any identification based solely on such literature must be considered tentative.

Acanthoceras	Bourrelly (1981).
Anabaena	Baker (1991).
Ankistrodesmus	Dillard (1990).
Audouinella	Entwisle (1989a); Entwisle and Kraft (1984).
Aulacoseira	Hustedt (1930); Hustedt (1961–66); Krammer and Lange-Bartalot (1991); Sullivan, Saunders and Welsh (1988); Thomas (1983).
Batrachospermum	Entwisle (1989a); Entwisle (1989c); Entwisle (1992); Entwisle (1993); Entwisle and Kraft (1984); Necchi and Entwisle (1990).
Bostrychia	Entwisle and Kraft (1984); King and Puttock (1989).
Botrydium	Bold and Wynne (1985).
Botryococcus	Dillard (1989a).
Bulbochaete	Dillard (1989a); Mrozinska (1985); Tiffany (1930).
Caloglossa	Entwisle and Kraft (1984); King and Puttock (1989).
Chaetophora	Entwisle (1989a); Hazen (1902).
Chara	Moore (1986); Raam (1995); Wood (1971); Wood and Imahori (1964–65).
Chlamydomonas	Ettl (1970, 1976, 1983).
Chroodactylon	Bourrelly (1985); Entwisle (1989a); Entwisle and Kraft (1984).
Chrysonephele	Pipes, Tyler and Leedale (1989).
Cladophora	Entwisle (1989a); Entwisle (1989c); van den Hoek (1963); van den Hoek (1982); Womersley (1984).
Closterium	Croasdale and Flint (1986).
Coleochaete	Bold and Wynne (1985); Dillard (1989b).
Coleodesmium	Bourrelly (1985); Entwisle (1989a).
Compsopogon	Entwisle (1989a); Entwisle and Kraft (1984); Entwisle and Price (1992); Krishnamurthy (1962).

Cosmarium	Croasdale and Flint (1988); Ling and Tyler (1986); Prescott *et al.* (1981); Thomasson (1986).
Cryptomonas	Javornický (1967).
Cyclotella	Krammer and Lange-Bertalot (1991).
Cylindrocapsa	Bourrelly (1990); Dillard (1989b).
Dichotomosiphon	Bold and Wynne (1985)
Dictyosphaerium	Ettl (1983).
Dinobryon	Croome *et al.* (1988b); Huber-Pestalozzi (1941).
Draparnaldia	Entwisle (1989a); Forest (1956); Smith (1950).
Ectocarpus	West and Kraft (1996).
Elakatothrix	Hindak (1962).
Enteromorpha	Womersley (1984).
Euglena	Buetow (1968); Pringsheim (1956).
Fragilaria	Krammer and Lange-Bertalot (1991).
Gomphonema	as for *Aulacoseira.*
Gonium	Dillard (1989a).
Hildenbrandia	Entwisle and Kraft (1984).
Hyalotheca	Ling and Tyler (1986).
Hydrodictyon	Coffey and Miller (1988); May (1982); Playfair (1914).
Klebsormidium	Brown and Hellebust (1980); Dillard (1989b); Silva *et al.* (1972).
Loefgrenia	Bourrelly (1985); Entwisle (1989a); Entwisle (1990a).
Lyngbya	as for *Schizothrix.*
Mallomonas	Asmund and Kristiansen (1986); Croome and Tyler (1985); Dürrschmidt and Croome (1985); Siver (1991); Takahashi (1978); Wujek and O'Kelly (1992).
Micractinium	Korschikov (1953).
Micrasterias	Sarim and Faridi (1992); Thomasson (1986).
Microcoleus	as for *Schizothrix*
Microcystis	Baker (1992); Bourrelly (1985); May (1974); May (1978); Victoria, Health Department (1990).
Microspora	Entwisle (1989a); Hazen (1902); Prescott (1962).
Monostroma	Golden and Garbary (1984); Womersley (1984).
Mougeotia	as for *Zygnema.*
Nitella	as for *Chara*; Casanova (1991); Hotchkiss and Imahori (1988a); Hotchkiss and Imahori (1988b).
Nodularia	Baker (1991); Bourrelly (1985); Desikachary (1959).
Nostoc	Bourrelly (1985); Desikachary (1959); Prescott (1962).
Oedogonium	Entwisle (1989a); Gonzalves (1981); Hirn (1900); Mrozinska (1985); Scott and Prescott (1958); Tiffany (1930).
Oocystis	Komárek and Fott (1983).
Oscillatoria	as for *Schizothrix.*

Palmellopsis	Bold and Wynne (1985); Entwisle (1989a), Ettl and Gärtner (1988).
Palmodictyon	Korshikov (1953); Smith (1950).
Parallela	Entwisle (1989a).
Pediastrum	Parra Barrientos (1979); Sulek (1969).
Peridinium	Popovsky and Pfiester (1990).
Phacus	Huber-Pestalozzi (1955).
Phormidium	as for *Schizothrix*.
Pithophora	Entwisle and Price (1992).
Pseudanabaena	Anagnostidis and Komárek (1988); Baker (1992).
Pseudosphaerocystis	Ettl and Gärtner (1988).
Psilosiphon	Entwisle (1989b).
Ptilothamnion	Bourrelly (1985); Cribb (1965).
Radiofilum	Dillard (1989b); Ling and Tyler (1986).
Rhizoclonium	Entwisle (1989a); Koster (1955); Nienhuis (1974); Womersley (1984).
Rivularia	Bourrelly (1985); Desikachary (1959).
Scenedesmus	Hegewald, et al. (1990).
Schizochlamys	Dillard (1989a); Smith (1950).
Schizomeris	Mattox, Stewart and Floyd (1974); Smith (1950).
Schizothrix	Anagnostidis and Komárek (1988); Baker (1992); Desikachary (1959).
Scytonema	Bourrelly (1985); Desikachary (1959).
Sphaeroplea	Bourrelly (1990); Dillard (1989b); Smith (1950).
Spirogyra	as for *Zygnema*; Pigram (1909).
Spirulina	as for *Schizothrix*
Staurastrum	Croasdale, et al. (1994); Thomasson (1986).
Stichococcus	Bold and Wynne (1985); Brown and Hellebust (1980).
Stigeoclonium	Entwisle (1989a); Entwisle (1989c); Islam (1963); Simons *et al.* (1986).
Stigonema	Bourrelly (1985); Desikachary (1959).
Synura	Croome and Tyler (1985); Nicholls and Gerrath (1985); Peterfi and Momeu (1977).
Tabellaria	as for *Aulacoseira*.
Tetraspora	Dillard (1989a); Ettl and Gärtner (1988); Korshikov (1953).
Tetrasporidium	Bourrelly (1988); Bourrelly (1990); Calado and Rino (1993); Couté and Tracanna (1981); Fott *et al.* (1965); Iyengar (1932).
Tetrasporopsis	Entwisle (1989a); Entwisle and Andersen (1990); Tschermak-Woess and Kusel-Fetzmann (1992).
Tolypothrix	Bourrelly (1985); Desikachary (1959).
Trachelomonas	Huber-Pestalozzi (1955).

Tribonema	Entwisle (1989a); Hazen (1902).
Ulothrix	Entwisle (1989a); Dillard (1989b); Lokhorst and Vroman (1972); Lokhorst and Vroman (1974a); Lokhorst and Vroman (1974b).
Urosolenia	Krammer and Lange-Bertalot (1991).
Vaucheria	Entwisle (1987); Entwisle (1988a); Entwisle (1988b).
Volvox	Ettl (1983); Huber-Pestalozzi (1961).
Zygnema	Dillard (1990); Entwisle (1989a); Gauthier-Lièvre (1965); Kadlubowska (1984); Ling and Tyler (1986); Randhawa (1959); Skinner (1980); Skinner (1983); Transeau (1951).

References

Anagnostidis, K., and Komárek, J. (1988). Modern approach to the classification system of cyanophytes. 3 - Oscillatoriales. *Archiv für Hydrobiologia*, Supplement **80**, 327–472.

Asmund, B., and Kristiansen, J. (1986). The Genus *Mallomonas* (Chrysophyceae). *Opera Botanica* **85**, 1–128.

Baker, P. (1991). *Identification of Common Noxious Cyanobacteria. Part I - Nostocales*. Urban Water Research Association of Australia, Research Report no. 29.

Baker, P. (1992). *Identification of Common Noxious Cyanobacteria. Part II - Chroococcales, Oscillatoriales*. Urban Water Research Association of Australia, Research Report no. 46.

Berlyn, G. P., and Miksche, J. P. (1976). *Botanical Microtechnique and Cytochemistry*. Iowa State University Press, Ames, Iowa.

Bold, H. C., and Wynne, M. J. (1985). *Introduction to the Algae. Structure and Reproduction*. 2nd edn. Prentice-Hall, Englewood Cliffs, N.J.

Bourrelly, P. (1968). *Les Algues d'eau Douce. Initiation à la Systématique.* Vol. 2. *Les Algues Jaunes et Brunes*. N. Boubée, Paris.

Bourrelly, P. (1985). *Les Algues d'eau Douce, Initiation à la Systématique.* Vol 3. *Algues Bleues et Rouges.* Rev. edn. N. Boubée, Paris.

Bourrelly, P. (1988). *Compléments Les Algues d'eau Douce. Initiation à la Systématique.* Vol. 1. *Les Algues Vertes. Compléments à la 1re, 2e et 3e édition.* N. Boubée, Paris.

Bourrelly, P. (1990). *Les Algues d'eau Douce. Initiation à la Systématique.* Vol. 1. *Les Algues Vertes. Réimpression revue et augmentée.* N. Boubée, Paris.

Brown, L. M., and Hellebust, J. A. (1980). Some new taxonomic characteristics applied to *Stichococcus bacillaris* (Chlorophyceae). *Canadian Journal of Botany* **58**, 1405–1411.

Buetow, D. E. (1968). *The Biology of Euglena*. Vol. 1 and 2. Academic Press, New York.

Calado, A. J., and Rino, J. A. (1993). Observations and taxonomic considerations on a *Tetrasporidium* (Chlorophyta, Tetrasporales) found in Portugal. *Cryptogamie: Algologie* **13**(3), 157–167.

Casanova, M. T. (1991). An SEM study of developmental variation in oospore wall ornamentation of three *Nitella* species (Charophyta) in Australia. *Phycologia* **30**, 237–242.

Chapman, V. J., and Chapman, D. J. (1973). *The Algae.* 2nd edn. Macmillan Press, London.

Christensen, T. (1980–1994). *Algae A Taxonomic Survey* AiO Print Ltd, Odense.

Coffey, B. T., and Miller, S. T. (1988). *Hydrodictyon reticulatum* L. Lagerheim (Chlorophyta): a new genus record from New Zealand. *New Zealand Journal of Botany* **26**, 317–320.

Cooke, M. C. (1882–1884). *British Fresh-water Algae.* Vols 1 and 2. Williams and Norgate, Edinburgh.

Couté, A., and Tracanna, B. (1981). Sur la présence en France de *Tetrasporidium javanicum* Moebius (Chlorophyta, Euchlorophyceae, Tetrasporales) et sa position systématique. *Cryptogamie: Algologie* **2**, 209–219.

Cribb, A. B. (1965). *Anfractutofilum umbracolens gen. et sp. nov.*, a freshwater red alga from Queensland. *Proceedings of the Royal Society of Qld.* **76**, 93–95.

Croasdale, H., and Flint, E. A. (1986). *Flora of New Zealand. Freshwater Algae, Chlorophyta, Desmids with Ecological Comments on their Habitats.* Vol. 1. V. R. Ward, Government Printer, Wellington.

Croasdale, H., and Flint, E. A. (1988). *Flora of New Zealand. Freshwater Algae, Chlorophyta, Desmids with Ecological Comments on their Habitats.* Vol. 2. *Actinotaenium, Cosmarium, Cosmodcladium, Spinocosmarium, Xanthidium.* Botany Division, D.S.I.R., Christchurch.

Croasdale, H., Flint E. A., and Racine, M. M. (1994). *Flora of New Zealand, Desmids.* Vol. 3. Manaaki Whenua Press, Lincoln.

Croome, R. L., and Tyler, P. A. (1985). Distribution of Silica-scaled Chrysophyceae (Paraphysomonadaceae and Mallomonadaceae) in Australian Inland Waters. *Australian Journal of Marine and Freshwater Research* **36**, 839–853.

Croome, R. L., and Tyler, P. A. (1988a), Further observations of silica-scaled Chrysophyceae (Paraphysomonadaceae and Mallomonadaceae) from Australian freshwaters. *Nova Hedwigia* **46**, 481–489.

Croome, R. L., Ling, H. U., and Tyler, P. A. (1988b), *Dinobryon unguentariforme* (Chrysophyceae), a new species from Australia. *British Phycologia Journal* **23**, 129–133.

Day, S. A., Wickham, R. P., Entwisle T. J., and Tyler, P. A. (1995). *Bibliographic Checklist of Non-marine Algae in Australia.* Australian Biological Resources Study, Canberra.

Desikachary, T. V. (1959). *Cyanophyta.* Indian Council of Agricultural Research, New Delhi.

Dillard, G. E. (1989a). Freshwater algae of the southeastern United States. Part 1. Chlorophyceae: Volvocales, Tetrasporales and Chlorococcales. *Bibliotheca Phycologica* **81**.

Dillard, G. E. (1989b). Freshwater algae of the southeastern United States. Part 2. Chlorophyceae: Ulotrichales, Microsporales, Cylindrocapsales, Sphaeropleales, Chaetophorales, Cladophorales, Schizogoniales, Siphonales and Oedogoniales. *Bibliotheca Phycologica* **83**.

Dillard, G. E. (1990). Freshwater algae of the southeastern United States. Part 2. Chlorophyceae: Zygnematales: Zygnemataceae, Mesotaeniaceae and Desmidiaceae (Section 1). *Bibliotheca Phycologica* **85**.

Dürrschmidt, M., and Croome, R. L. (1985), Mallomonadaceae (Chrysophyceae) from Malaysia and Australia. *Nordic Journal Botany* **5**, 285–298.

Entwisle, T. J. (1987). An evaluation of taxonomic characters in the subsection Sessiles, section Corniculatae, of *Vaucheria* (Vaucheriaceae, Chrysophyta). *Phycologia* **26**, 297–321.

Entwisle, T. J. (1988a). A monograph of *Vaucheria* (Vaucheriaceae, Chrysophyta) in south-eastern Australia. *Australian Systematic Botany* **1**, 1–77.

Entwisle, T. J. (1988b). An evaluation of taxonomic characters in the *Vaucheria prona* complex (Vaucheriaceae, Chrysophyta). *Phycologia* **26**, 183–200.

Entwisle, T. J. (1989a). Macroalgae in the Yarra River basin: flora and distribution. *Proceedings of the Royal Society of Victoria* **101**, 1–76.

Entwisle, T. J. (1989b). *Psilosiphon scoparium* gen. et sp. nov. (Lemaneaceae), a new red alga from south-eastern Australian streams. *Phycologia* **28**, 469–475.

Entwisle, T. J. (1989c). Phenology of the *Cladophora-Stigeoclonium* community in two urban creeks of Melbourne. *Australian Journal of Marine and Freshwater Research* **40**, 471–489.

Entwisle, T. J. (1992). The setaceous species of *Batrachospermum* (Rhodophyta): a re-evaluation of *B. atrum* (Hudson) Harvey and *B. puiggarianum* Grunow including the description of *B. diatyches sp. nov.* from Tasmania, Australia. *Muelleria* **7**, 425–445.

Entwisle, T. J. (1993). The discovery of Batrachospermalean taxa (Rhodophyta) in Australia and New Zealand. *Muelleria* **8**, 5–16.

Entwisle, T. J. (Ed.) (1994). *Aquatic Cryptograms of Australia. A guide to the larger fungi, lichens, macroalgae, liverworts and mosses of Australian Inland waters.* Australian Society for Limnology, Special publication No. 10, Melbourne.

Entwisle, T. J., and Andersen, R. A. (1990). A re-examination of *Tetrasporopsis* (Chrysophyceae) and a description of *Dermatochrysis* gen. nov. (Chrysophyceae): a monostromatic alga lacking cell walls. *Phycologia* **29**, 263–274.

Entwisle, T. J., and Kraft, G. T. (1984). Survey of freshwater red algae (Rhodophyta) of south-eastern Australia. *Australian Journal of Marine and Freshwater Research* **35**, 213–259.

Entwisle, T. J., and Price I. R. (1992). New records of two potential weed species of freshwater macroalgae from Queensland. *Proceedings of the Royal Society of Queensland* **102**, 57–63.

Ettl, H. (1970). *Die Gattung Chloromonas* Gobi emend. Wille. *Beihefte zur Nova Hedwigia* **34**.

Ettl, H. (1976). *Die Gattung Chlamydomonas* Ehrenburg. *Beihefte zur Nova Hedwigia* **49**.

Ettl, H. (1983). Chlorophyta. I. Phytomonadina. In *Süsswasserflora von Mitteleuropa* **9** (Eds H. Ettl., J. Gerloff, H. Heynig and D. Mollenhouer) Gustav Fischer Verlag, Stuttgart.

Ettl, H., and Gärtner, G. (1988). Chlorophyta 2. Tetrasporales, Chlorococcales, Gloeodendrales. In *Süsswasserflora von Mitteleuropa*. **10** (Eds H. Ettl, J. Gerloff, H. Heynig and D. Mollenhaur) Gustav Fischer Verlag, Stuttgart.

Fott, B., Novakova, M., and Kalina, T. (1965). Morphology, Reproduction and Occurrence of a Tropical Alga, *Tetrasporidium javanicum* Mobius (Chlorophyceae). *Preslia* **37**, 380–386.

Fritsch, F. E. (1935). *The Structure and Reproduction of the Algae.* Vol. 1. Cambridge University Press, Cambridge.

Fritsch, F. E. (1945). *The Structure and Reproduction of the Algae.* Vol. 2. Cambridge University Press, Cambridge.

Gauthier-Lièvre, L. (1965). Zygnémacées Africaines. *Beihefte zur Nova Hedwigia* **20**.

Golden, L., and Garbary, D. (1984). Studies on *Monostroma* (Monostromataceae, Chlorophyta) in British Columbia with emphasis on spore release. *Japanese Journal of Phycology* **32**, 319–332.

Gonzalves, E. A. (1981). *Oedogoniales.* New Delhi, Indian Council of Agricultural Research.

Hazen, T. E. (1902). The Ulotrichaceae and Chaetophoraceae of the United States. *Memoirs of the Torrey Botanical Club* **11**, 135–250, pls 20–42.

Hegewald, E., Hindak, F., and Schnepf, E. (1990). Studies on the genus *Scenedesmus* Meyen (Chlorophyceae, Chlorococcales) from South India, with special reference to the cell wall ultrastructure. *Beihefte zur Nova Hedwigia* **99**.

Hindak, F. (1962). Systematische Revision der Gattungen *Fusola* Snow und *Elakatothrix* Wille. *Preslia* **34**, 277–292.

Hirn, K. E. (1900). Monographie und Iconographie der Oedogonioceen. *Acta Societatis Scirntierum Fennicae* **27**, 1–394. [Reprinted 1960. Historiae Naturalis Classica. Vol. 17. (Eds J. Cramer and H.K. Swann).]

Hoek, C. van den (1963). *Revision of the European species of Cladophora.* Leiden 1963. [Reprinted 1976 by Otto Koeltz Science Publishers, Koenigstein, Germany.]

Hoek, C. van den (1982). *A Taxonomic Revision of the American Species of Cladophora (Chlorophyceae) in the North Atlantic Ocean and their Geographic Distribution.* North-Holland Publishing Co., Amsterdam, Oxford, New York.

Hotchkiss, A. T., and Imahori, K. (1988a). A new species of *Nitella* (Characeae) belonging to the pluricellulate species group in Australia. *Proceedings of the Linnaean Society of New South Wales* **110**, 175–185.

Hotchkiss, A. T., and Imahori, K. (1988b). Additional observations on *Nitella verticillata* (Characeae) from a new locality in New South Wales. *Proceedings of the Linnaean Society of New South Wales* **110**, 187–191.

Huber-Pestalozzi, G. (1941). Das Phytoplankton des Süsswassers. Chrysophyceen. *Die Binnengewässer* **16**, Teil 2(1).

Huber-Pestalozzi, G. (1955). Das Phytoplankton des Süsswassers. Euglenophyceen. *Die Binnengewässer* **16**, Teil 4.

Huber-Pestalozzi, G. (1961). Das Phytoplankton des Süsswassers. Chlorophyceae: Volvocales. *Die Binnengewässer* **16**, Teil 5.

Hustedt, F. (1930). Bacillariophyta. In *Die Süsswasserflora Mitteleuropas*. **2**. (Ed. A. Pascher) G. Fischer, Jena.

Hustedt, F. (1961–66). Die Kieselalgen Deutschlands, Österreichs und der Schweiz unter Berücksichtigung der übrigen Länder Europas sowie der angrenzenden Meeresgebiete. In *Kryptogamenflora von Deutschland, Österreich und der Schweiz* **7**(3). (Ed. L. Rabenhorst) Akademische Verlagsgesellschaft Geest and Portig, Leipzig.

Islam, A. K. M. N. (1963). A revision of the genus *Stigeoclonium. Beihefte Zur Nova Hedwigia* **10**.

Iyengar, M. O. P. (1932). Two little known genera of green algae (*Tetrasporidium* and *Ecallocystis*). *Annals of Botany* **46**, 191–227.

Javornický, P. (1967). Some interesting algal flagellates. *Folia Geobotanica et Phytotaxonomica* **2**, 43–67, pl. 2–9

Johansson, D. A. (1940). *Plant Microtechnique*. McGraw-Hill, New York.

Jones, G. (1994). Blue-green algae. In *Waterplants in Australia*, 3rd edn. (By G. R. Sainty and S. W. L. Jacobs) Sainty and Associates, Potts Point.

Kadlubowska, J. Z. (1984). Chlorophyta. VIII. Conjugatophyceae. 1. Zygnemales. In *Süsswasserflora von Mitteleuropa* **16**. (Eds H. Ettl. J. Gerloff, H. Heynig, and D. Mollenhauer) Gustav Fischer Verlag, Stuttgart.

King, R. J., and Puttock, C. F. (1989). Morphology and taxonomy of *Bostrychia* and *Stictosiphonia* (Rhodomelaceae/Rhodophyta). *Australian Systematic Botany* **2**, 1–73.

Komárek, J., and Fott, B. (1983). *Das* Phytoplankton des Süsswassers. Chlorophyceae: Chlorococcales. *Die Binnengewässer* **16**, Teil 7(1).

Korshikov, O. A. (1953). *The Freshwater Algae of the Ukrainian SSR*. **5**. *Sub-class Protococcineae, Vacuolales and Protococcales*. [Reprinted 1987; translated by J. W. G. Lund and W. Tylka. Bishen Singh Mahendra Pal Singh and Koeltz Scientific Books, Dehra Dun, India.]

Koster, J. Th. (1955). The genus *Rhizoclonium* Kütz in the Netherlands. *Pubblicazioni Stazione zoologica Napoli* **27**, 335–357.

Krammer, K., and Lange-Bertalot, H. (1991). Bacillariophyceae. In *Süsswasserflora von Mittleuropa* **2/3**, Teil 4. (Eds H. Ettl, J. Gerloff, H. Heynig and D. Mollenhaur) Gustav Fischer Verlag, Stuttgart.

Krishnamurthy, V. (1962). The morphology and taxonomy of the genus *Compsopogon* Montagne. *Botanical Journal of the Linnaean Society* **58**, 207–222.

Lee, R. E. (1989). *Phycology*. 2nd edn. Cambridge University Press, Cambridge.

Ling, H. U., and Tyler, P. A. (1986). *A Limnological survey of the Magela Creek System, Alligator Rivers Region, Northern Territory Algae of the Region (excluding Diatoms)*. Australian Publishing Service, Canberra.

Lokhorst, G. M., and Vroman, M. (1972). Taxonomic study on three freshwater *Ulothrix* species. *Acta Botanica Neerlandica* **21**, 449–480.

Lokhorst, G. M., and Vroman, M. (1974a). Taxonomic studies on the genus *Ulothrix* (Ulotrichales, Chlorophyceae). II. *Acta Botanica Neerlandica* **23**, 369–398.

Lokhorst, G. M., and Vroman, M. (1974b). Taxonomic studies on the genus *Ulothrix* (Ulotrichales, Chlorophyceae). III. *Acta Botanica Neerlandica* **23**, 561–602.

Mattox, K. R., Stewart, K. D., and Floyd, G. L. (1974). The cytology and classification of *Schizomeris leibleinii* (Chlorophyceae). I. The vegetative thallus. *Phycologia* **13**, 63–69.

May, V. (1974). Suppression of blue-green algal blooms in Braidwood Lagoon with Alum. *Journal of the Australian Institute of Agricultural Science* **40**, 54–57.

May, V. (1978). Areas of recurrence of toxic algae within Burrinjuck Dam, NSW, Australia. *Telopea* **1**, 295–313.

May, V. (1982). Freshwater algae. In *Waterplants of NSW.* (By G. R. Sainty and S. W. L. Jacobs) Water Resources Commission NSW, Sydney.

Moore, J. A. (1986). *Charophytes of Great Britain and Ireland.* Botanical Society of the British Isles, London.

Mrozinska, T. (1985). Chlorophyta VI. Oedogoniophyceae: Oedogoniales. In *Süsswasserflora von Mitteleuropa.* **14** (Eds H. Ettl., J. Gerloff, H. Heynig and D. Mollenhouer) Gustav Fischer Verlag, Stuttgart.

Necchi, O. Jr, and Entwisle, T. J. (1990). A reappraisal of generic and subgeneric classification in the Batrachospermaceae (Rhodophyta). *Phycologia* **29**, 478–488.

Nicholls, K. H., and Gerrath, J. F. (1985). The taxonomy of *Synura* (Chrysophyceae) in Ontario with special reference to taste and odor in water supplies. *Canadian Journal of Botany* **63**, 1482–1493.

Nienhuis, P. H. (1974). Variability in the life cycle of *Rhizoclonium riparium* (Roth) Harv. (Chlorophyceae: Cladophorales) under Dutch estuarine conditions. *Hydrobiological Bulletin* **8**, 172–178.

Parra Barrientos, O. O. (1979). Revision der Gattung *Pediastrum* Meyen (Chlorophyta). *Bibliotheca Phycologia* **48**.

Peterfi, L. S., and Momeu, L. (1977). Remarks on the taxonomy of some *Synura* species based on the fine structure of scales. *Studii si Comunicari, Muzel Stiintel Naturii. Bioliologie* **21**, 15–23.

Pigram, F. (1909). The Queensland *Spirogyra. Queensland Naturalist* **1**, 96–103, pl. 1.

Pipes, L. D., Tyler, P. A., and Leedale, G. F. (1989). *Chrysonephele palustris gen. et sp. nov.* (Chrysophyceae), a new colonial chrysophyte from Tasmania. *Nova Hedwigia* **95**, 81–97.

Playfair, G. I. (1914). Contributions to a knowledge of the biology of the Richmond River, NSW. *Proceedings of the Linnaean Society of New South Wales* **39**, 93–151, pl. 2–8.

Popovsky, J., and Pfiester, L. A. (1990). Dinophyceae (Dinoflagellida). In *Süsswasserflora von Mitteleuropa* **6**. (Eds H. Ettl, J. Gerloff, H. Heynig and D. Mollenhaur) Gustav Fischer Verlag, Jena.

Prescott, G. W. (1954). *How to Know the Freshwater Algae.* Wm. C. Brown, Dubuque, Iowa.

Prescott, G. W. (1962). *Algae of the Western Great Lakes, with an Illustrated Key to the Genera of Desmids and Freshwaer Diatoms.* Rev. edn. [Reprinted 1982 by Otto Koeltz Science Publishers, Koenigstein, Germany]

Prescott, G. W., Croasdale, H. T., Vinyard, W. C., and Bicudo, C. E. de M. (1981). *A Synopsis of North American Desmids. Part. II. Desmidiaceae: Placodermae. Section 3.* University of Nebraska Press, Lincoln and London.

Prescott, G. W. (1982). *Algae of the Western Great Lakes Area.* Revised edn, Otto Koeltz Science Publishers, Koenigstein, Germany.

Pringsheim, E. G. (1956). Contributions towards a Monograph of the genus *Euglena*. *Nova Acta Leopoldina* **18**.

Raam, J. C. (1995). The Characeae of Tasmania. *Beihefte zur Nova Hedwigia* **110**.

Randhawa, M. S. (1959). *Zygnemaceae*. Indian council of Agricultural Research, New Delhi.

Sarim, F. M., and Faridi, M. A. F. (1992). *Micrasterias* in Pakistan. *Pakistan Journal of Science and Industrial Research* **35**, 39–42.

Scott, A. M., and Prescott, G. W. (1958). Some freshwater algae from Arnhemland in the Northern Territory of Australia. In *Records of the American-Australian Scientific expedition to Arnhemland. 3. Botany and Plant Ecology.* (Eds R. L. Specht and C. P. Mountford) Melbourne University Press, Melbourne.

Silva, P. C., Mattox, K. R., and Blackwell, W. H. Jr. (1972). The generic name *Hormidium* as applied to green algae. *Taxon* **21**, 639–645.

Simons, J., van Beem, A. P., and de Vries, P. J. R. (1986). Morphology of the prostrate thallus of *Stigeoclonium* (Chlorophyceae, Chaetophorales) and its taxonomic implications. *Phycologia* **25**, 210–220.

Siver, P. A. (1991). The Biology of Mallomonas: Morphology, Taxonomy and Ecology. *Developments in Hydrobiology* **63**, 1–230.

Skinner, S. (1980). New records of Zygnemaphyceae and Oedogoniaceae (Chlorophyta) from northern New South Wales. *Proceedings of the Linnaean Society of New South Wales* **104**, 245–264.

Skinner, S. (1983). Some fresh water Chlorophyta from the Bool lagoon system in southeastern South-Australia. *Transactions of the Royal Society of South Australia* **107**, 223–230.

Smith, G. M. (1950). *Freshwater Algae of the United States.* 2nd edn. McGraw-Hill, New York.

Starmach, K. (Ed.) (1968–1983). *Flora Slodkowodna Polski.* 1–12, Polska Akademia Nauk, Instytut Botaniki, Panstwowe Wydawnictwo Naukowe.

Sulek, J. (1969). Taxonomische Übersicht der Gattung *Pediastrum* Meyen. In *Studies in Phycology* (Ed. B. Fott) Academia, Prague.

Sullivan, C., Saunders, J., and Welsh, D. (1988). *The Phytoplankton of the River Murray, 1980–1985.* Water, Materials and Environmental Science Branch Report no. 92, Rural Water Commission of Victoria.

Sze, P. (1986). *A Biology of the Algae.* Wm C. Brown, Dubuque, Iowa.

Takahashi, E. (1978). *Electron Microscopical studies of the Synuraceae (Chrysophyceae) in Japan, Taxonomy and Ecology.* Tokai University Press, Tokyo.

Thomas, D. P. (1983). *A Limnological Survey of the Alligator Rivers Region. I. Diatoms (Bacillariophyceae) of the Region.* Supervising Scientist for the Alligator Rivers Region Research Report 3, part I.

Thomasson, K. (1986). Algal vegetation in North Australian billabongs, *Nova Hedwigia* **42**, 301–378.

Tiffany, L. H. (1930). *The Oedogoniaceae. A Monograph.* Published by author, Columbus, Ohio.

Transeau, E. N. (1951). *The Zygnemataceae.* The Ohio State University Press, Columbus, Ohio.

Tschermak-Woess, E., and Kusel-Fetzmann, E. (1992). A new find of *Tetrasporopsis fuscescens* (A. Braun ex Kützing) Lemmermann (Chrysophyta) in Austria, and some additional observations. *Archiv für Protistenkunde* **142**, 157–165.

Tyler, P.A., and Wickham, R.P. (1988). Yan Yean Revisited — a bicentennial window on Australian freshwater algae. *British Phycological Journal* **23**, 105–114.

Victoria, Health Department (1990). *Blue-green Algae in Drinking Water Supplies.* [An information package prepared by the Working Party of Blue-green Algae in Water Supplies under the auspices of the Health Department Victoria.]

West, G. S., and Fritsch, F. E. (1926). *A Treatise on the Freshwater Algae.* [Revised by F. E. Fritsch]. Cambridge Unversity Press, Cambridge.

West, J. A., and Kraft, G. T. (1996). *Ectocarpus siliculosus* (Dillwyn) Lyngbye from Hopkins River Falls, Victoria — The first record of a freshwater brown alga in Australia. *Muelleria* **9**, 29–33.

Womersley, H. B. S. (1984). *The Marine Benthic Flora of Southern Australia. Part 1.* Government Printer, Adelaide.

Wood, R. D., and Imahori, K. (1964–1965). *A Revision of the Characeae.* 2 vols. Weinheim, Stuttgart.

Wood, R. D. (1971). Characeae of Australia. *Nova Hedwigia* **22**, 1–120.

Wujek, D. E., and O'Kelly, C. J. (1992). Silica-scaled Chrysophyceae (Mallomonadaceae and Paraphysomonadaceae) from New Zealand freshwaters. *New Zealand Journal of Botany* **30**, 405–414.

Index